Royal
Botanic Garden
Edinburgh

World of
Plants
Stories of Survival

Dr Alexandra Davey

MIX
Paper from
responsible sources
FSC® C115556

1056915
Printed on Carbon Captured paper

Printed by McAllister Litho Glasgow Ltd

ISBN: 978-1-910877-40-1

© Royal Botanic Garden Edinburgh, 2021.
Published by the Royal Botanic Garden Edinburgh
20A Inverleith Row, Edinburgh, EH3 5LR

www.rbge.org.uk

Proceeds from sales of this book will be used to support the work of the
Royal Botanic Garden Edinburgh.

The Royal Botanic Garden Edinburgh is a Non Departmental Public Body (NDPB)
sponsored and supported through Grant-in-Aid by the
Scottish Government's Environment and Forestry Directorate (ENFOR).

The Royal Botanic Garden Edinburgh is a
Charity registered in Scotland (number SC007983).

Edited by Elanor Clarke
Proofread by Erica Schwarz
Designed by Caroline Muir
Assistant Andrew Lindsay

Contents

Introduction

Plants are experts at survival. Rooted to the spot and unable to flee from danger, they have evolved an astonishing range of defensive strategies, from vicious spines and lethal poisons to fireproof coats and emergency food stores.

However, for many plants, survival has become increasingly difficult. Evolution can't keep pace with the array of challenges they face today, including emerging pests and pathogens, invasive weeds, wildfire, habitat destruction and climate change.

Humans are intricately linked to the plant kingdom. The interconnections between species and ecosystem conservation, climate change mitigation, food security, sustainable livelihoods, and our health and wellbeing are becoming clearer by the day. Botanic gardens strengthen these connections: providing spaces where people can spend time among plants; informing and engaging with visitors of all ages about the global challenges facing the natural world; and working to better understand and protect the world's plants.

The Royal Botanic Garden Edinburgh is a world leader in conservation horticulture and custodian of a collection of more than 13,500 species from around the world, growing across four remarkably diverse Scottish Gardens – Benmore, Dawyck, Edinburgh and Logan. We acknowledge the historic colonial links of this collection, and believe that this makes our responsibility to care for them, share them, use them wisely, and where possible repatriate them, all the greater.

Our Living Collection includes over 450 species known to be threatened with extinction – and that is likely a huge underestimate. For some species, such as the endangered *Begonia samhaensis*, these plants are the only individuals outside their natural habitat, and thus their only insurance against extinction should the wild population be destroyed.

World of Plants, Stories of Survival is your invitation to meet some of the world's rarest and most threatened species in our Living Collection. Here we find botanical equivalents of the deep-sea coelacanth – considered extinct, then joyously rediscovered – and plant versions of the passenger pigeon – once widespread but collected to near-extinction. There are species from as far afield as Canada and New Zealand, Chile and Japan. There are tiny mosses and the largest tree on Earth.

Some have already been lost from the wild; many are just clinging on. Several are slowly but surely recovering, while others are in increasing peril as climate change accelerates or introduced pests and diseases spread rapidly through their range. For all our plants, we have much more to learn as we race to halt extinction and restore fully functional ecosystems.

Conserving species in botanic gardens – '*ex situ*' – is a last resort, and no substitute for action to control the underlying global issues. It is by far easiest and most successful to safeguard species *in situ*, in their natural habitat, alongside all the organisms with which they naturally coexist. For this reason, we are actively involved in collaborative research, training and conservation in more than 40 countries around the world. Engaging in both *in-situ* and *ex-situ* conservation together provides a 'belt and braces' to save the rarest species from extinction.

One of the Garden's longest-running global initiatives is the International Conifer Conservation Programme, which monitors the status of the world's 600 or more conifer species, over one third of which are threatened, and 15 of which can be seen in this book. The Programme works with local and international partners to protect and restore ecosystems around the world – such as the incredible *Araucaria araucana* (*pehuén* or monkey puzzle) forests of Chile's Reserva Nasampulli – and to manage a pioneering network of over 200 'safe sites' across the British Isles, where conifers are cultivated *ex situ* with the long-term aim of reinforcing wild populations.

Threatened species are not confined to far-flung parts of the world. Closer to home in Scotland we find communities of cryptogams (fungi, algae, lichens, and the bryophytes: mosses, liverworts and hornworts) that are extraordinarily diverse, specialist and globally rare, not to mention vital to global nutrient cycles. In *World of Plants, Stories of Survival*, we share the stories of three Scottish cryptogams, alongside Britain's rarest fern, two trees found only in the UK, and several nationally threatened species that we are working to protect.

World of Plants is organised following an idiosyncratic ranking of how well the plants have bounced back from the brink – the strength of their survival story, if you will. So *Juniperus saxicola*, at 100, is assessed as critically endangered and declining, where previously it was only vulnerable, has only around 50 wild plants left, is maintained in few *ex-situ* collections, and is increasingly at risk from landslides, fire, and competition from introduced invasive species. As for number one? You'll have to wait and see!

Forty per cent of the world's plant species are now threatened with extinction, and many have already been lost, but the stories in this book provide a glimpse of the amazing range of beauty and potential that remains. These are stories of resilience and restoration, of what can be achieved when individuals, communities, organisations, governments and international bodies pull together. Stories of survival, in which we can all play a part.

Welcome to Our World of Plants

The Royal Botanic Garden Edinburgh is spread over 112 hectares at four unique sites: Benmore, Dawyck, Edinburgh and Logan.

Benmore Botanic Garden near Dunoon in Argyll became part of the organisation in 1929, and is the largest site, covering nearly 50 hectares. With its typically wet, west-coast climate and mountainous terrain it is ideal for our Chilean, Himalayan and Japanese plants, including a huge collection of *Rhododendron.* Large numbers of threatened conifers can be found here – not least an iconic avenue of 49 giant redwoods. In the restored Victorian Fernery the lush greenness is set off – when in flower – by bright magenta *Valdivia gayana.*

Dawyck Botanic Garden at Stobo near Peebles in the Scottish Borders is our newest Garden, joining the estate in 1979. This Garden is home to one of Scotland's finest arboreta – containing many threatened trees – and is also famous for its snowdrops and *Meconopsis*, azalea terrace, and the world's first cryptogam sanctuary, Heron Wood.

The Royal Botanic Garden Edinburgh lies in the city's New Town, a site it has occupied since 1820. Its 25 hectares house, among others, a Rock Garden, Woodland Garden, rich Chinese Hillside, large *Rhododendron* collection, and many rare Scottish species. Edinburgh's heritage Glasshouses are a highlight for any visit. To protect the precious plants they contain, and reduce the Garden's energy consumption and carbon emissions, from 2021–2028 the Glasshouses are undergoing extensive refurbishment and redevelopment through a programme known as Edinburgh Biomes.

One of the most ambitious undertakings in the Garden's history, Edinburgh Biomes will involve the development of new research and education facilities, an efficient Energy Centre and secure Plant Health Hub, as well as a flagship new Glasshouse – The Frond – in conjunction with redevelopment of the existing Glasshouse range. The Glasshouses are closed to visitors during this time, so you may not be able to visit quite as many of our plants as you would like. We hope you'll bear with us during this exciting time, and we look forward to welcoming you back to our Glasshouses in the future.

Logan Botanic Garden near Stranraer in Dumfries and Galloway is our most tropical garden, and was gifted to the organisation in 1969. Warmed by the Gulf Stream, the site is ideally suited to species from Australia, New Zealand, South America and South Africa, which would not survive outside elsewhere in Scotland. From palms and tree ferns to giant echiums and foxgloves, it's well worth a visit to experience some of the world's most threatened plants.

Alongside each of the 100 species featured in *World of Plants, Stories of Survival* you can find information about its place in the Royal Botanic Garden Edinburgh's Living Collection. **Specimen notes** explain the history and origin of the plants in the Collection today. **Location** tells you where across our four Gardens they may be found.

Conservation status indicates the level of risk assigned in the International Union for Conservation of Nature's official *Red List of Threatened Species*. Unless otherwise specified this is a global assessment of threat. In order of severity, these are:

VU – vulnerable
EN – endangered
CR – critically endangered
EW – extinct in the wild

Outside this book you may also see the categories:

DD – data deficient
LC – least concern
NT – near threatened
EX – extinct

For more information about the Royal Botanic Garden Edinburgh and our Living Collection of plants, please visit **rbge.org.uk** or connect with us on social media.

Juniperus saxicola

Juniperus saxicola (Cupressaceae – cypress family) is a conifer found only in Cuba. Even here, it is confined to the Turquino massif in the Sierra Maestra, where it is known from three peaks in the Parque Nacional Turquino, in the south-east of the island. In total, only 53 trees are left in the wild.

All four juniper species found on the Caribbean islands are thought to have evolved from one North American species, *J. virginiana* (Virginia juniper or eastern red cedar), perhaps brought here as seeds in the stomachs or on the feet of birds, travelling first to the Bahamas, then on to Bermuda, Cuba, Jamaica and Hispaniola.

Juniperus saxicola grows in cloud forest or on ridges, rocky outcrops and in crevices – anywhere where it is hard for herbivores to get at the trees. With such a tiny number of individuals left, the species is highly susceptible to being wiped out by random catastrophic events such as landslides, as well as fire, tourism and encroachment by invasive species. These risks are compounded by their poor regeneration.

Many junipers produce prickly juvenile leaves in their formative years, to protect young plants from grazing. *Juniperus saxicola* is one of only four out of the more than 60 species of juniper to display this prickly foliage all its life – it has never been recorded as having the softer adult foliage. This state of perpetual youth might be considered a form of neoteny, a phenomenon more usually associated with animals such as the axolotl.

All Juniperus saxicola trees in the British Isles are descended from a single, ancient Cuban example.

All the *J. saxicola* plants in the British Isles are thought to be descendants of a single, old, wild Cuban tree. There are now several youngsters growing at Edinburgh and at other conservation safe sites around the UK.

Specimen notes | Grown from cuttings collected by the Royal Botanic Garden Edinburgh's Martin Gardner and colleagues from the University of Havana, in 2003 and 2006.

Location | Edinburgh (not on public display).

Conservation status | CR

Rhododendron multinervium

One of the most recognisable of plant genera (a genus is a taxonomic group of closely related plant species), the popular *Rhododendron* (Ericaceae – heath family) is far more varied than we may think. As well as the hardy shrubs planted in gardens across the UK, one third of all *Rhododendrons* – over 300 species – belong to the tropical Southeast Asian group known as *Vireya*. The Glasshouses at the Royal Botanic Garden Edinburgh hold the largest cultivated collection of *Vireyas* in the world.

One of these, *Rhododendron multinervium*, is so far thought to be restricted to Papua New Guinea, although as some plants occur close to the border with West Papua, Indonesia, it is possible the species may also extend across it. It is known from only five localities. *Rhododendron multinervium* can grow into a small tree. Its stunning tubular white flowers produce a scent that ranges from vanilla to frangipani, depending on who you ask. The epithet *multinervium* comes from the distinctive pattern of veins on the species' leaves.

These gorgeous white flowers have a scent reminiscent of vanilla!

The distribution of *R. multinervium* is limited to the alpine to sub-alpine high-altitude mainland of Papua New Guinea. From studying records at the National Herbarium (an organised collection of pressed, dried plant specimens and associated data) of Papua New Guinea, this species has historically been found in rather accessible parts of the forest, putting the plant at risk of impact from human activity. Of course, it may also be that these were the easiest places to collect plant specimens!

There are many threats to this *Rhododendron*. Its habitat is under great pressure and fragmented by fires, small-scale agriculture, and encroachment from human settlement. The increasing risk to the species can be seen in its rapid change of conservation status – from 'least concern' in 2015 to endangered in 2019. Unfortunately, many species do not have the luxury of being assessed so often – but *Rhododendrons* are the subject of intensive study by the Global Conservation Consortium for *Rhododendron*, of which the Royal Botanic Garden Edinburgh is a leading member.

Rhododendron multinervium flowers well in the Glasshouses at the Royal Botanic Garden Edinburgh. The oldest example in the Garden is more than 55 years old.

Specimen notes | Our oldest plant was collected in Papua New Guinea in 1965 by ornithologist Geoffrey Alton Craig Herklots (1902–1986). Two other plants were obtained from cultivated collections more recently.

Location | Edinburgh (Glasshouses).

Conservation status |

Chordospartium muritai

Sometimes known as the coastal tree broom, this relative of our Scotch broom (*Cytisus scoparius*) was first formally described according to western scientific convention in 1985 by New Zealand botanist Andrew Purdie (1940–1989), in the *New Zealand Journal of Botany*. At that time, only 28 plants were identified, across two sites. Today it is confined to just one of these – Clifford Bay, in Marlborough, South Island – where only 12 wild plants survive in a fragment of coastal forest.

An almost leafless tree (photosynthesis is carried out in the stems, reducing water losses in its dry, windy habitat) up to six metres tall, the coastal tree broom bears tiny but intricate pink and white pea-like flowers in spikes. Its epithet, *muritai*, comes from the Maori for 'sea breeze', and alludes to the plants' coastal habitat.

The coastal tree broom is one of two species of *Chordospartium* (Fabaceae – legume family), both of which are found only in New Zealand. *Chordospartium stevensonii*, the weeping tree broom, is classed as vulnerable, and is also known only from Marlborough. Some botanists now consider *Chordospartium* to be part of the larger genus *Carmichaelia*, on the basis of molecular genetic data. Here we follow the classification used in the International Union for Conservation of Nature (IUCN)'s *Red List of Threatened Species*.

The coastal tree broom's existence is threatened by herbivores, drought, erosion, competition from weeds, and fire. Every part of the plant is highly sought after by browsing animals, particularly goats, possums, hares and rabbits. Its location is designated a Scientific Reserve, to which access is restricted, but the population continues to decline.

Bearing virtually no leaves, all the photosynthesis in this plant occurs in the stems.

Specimen notes | Collected in New Zealand, received by the Royal Botanic Garden Edinburgh in 1998.

Location | Logan (easily visible near the Potting Shed Bistro in what is nicknamed the Salad Bar Border!).

Conservation status | CR

Adelanthus lindenbergianus

The liverwort *Adelanthus lindenbergianus* (Lindenberg's featherwort; Adelanthaceae) is very rare and endangered in Europe. It is found at only a handful of sites on the west coast of Ireland and two in Scotland: Beinn Bheigier, the highest summit on Islay, and another peak on the neighbouring island of Jura, some 15 kilometres away.

Our European Lindenberg's featherworts can usually be found in the globally rare oceanic-montane liverwort-rich heath. This community owes its continued existence to the notoriously wet climate of the British Isles' western uplands. Lindenberg's featherwort in particular is only partial to the very wettest, most western Scottish and Irish hills, where clouds travelling across the North Atlantic dump their loads on the waiting peaks.

Would the real Lindenberg's featherwort please stand up?

Outside Europe, Lindenberg's featherwort is thought to be doing rather better, and can be found across sub-Saharan Africa, the Indian Ocean islands of Madagascar, Reunion and Mauritius, and in Central and South America. However, research suggests that there are actually at least two 'cryptic' species here, morphologically near-identical, but evolutionarily separate. Genetic data suggests that the tropical American and South American populations are actually two different species, and nobody yet knows whether the African plants can be grouped with one of these, or are yet again different!

Within this complex picture, the Scottish and Irish plants also remain an enigma – research is underway at the Royal Botanic Garden Edinburgh to determine which of the world's populations is their closest relative, and ultimately which species they belong to, and therefore how threatened they are.

European Lindenberg's featherworts are at risk from overgrazing, muirburn or wildfire, and potentially climate change, compounded by the low number of individuals in each local population. Dramatic declines have happened at many of the Irish sites over recent years due to overgrazing by sheep – most notably in the Twelve Bens of Connemara, where the featherwort was previously abundant but is now confined to a single site. The main Scottish site on Islay is designated an Important Plant Area (IPA), but otherwise has no legal protection.

Specimen notes | 20 specimens from around the world can be seen in the Herbarium. The species is not yet in the Living Collection but is subject to intensive study by Royal Botanic Garden Edinburgh teams in the field.

Location | Edinburgh (Herbarium).

Conservation status | EN (Europe)

Pseudocyphellaria lacerata

The wonderfully named ragged specklebelly, *Pseudocyphellaria lacerata* (Lobariaceae) is a lichen known only from a scattering of highly threatened fragments of temperate rainforest – Scotland's answer to the tropical rainforest, and equally precious and threatened. This very rare complex organism seems to be reliant on a specialised habitat characterised by year-round mild temperatures and high humidity, termed a 'hyperoceanic' distribution.

The lichen – which comprises an intricate symbiosis between a cohabiting fungus and cyanobacterium – inhabits patches of ancient forest around the North Atlantic coasts of the UK, Norway and the Faroe Islands, the Azores and Madeira, the far-flung South Atlantic islands of Gough and Prince Edward, South Africa and Patagonia. In parts of its range, its available habitat has shrunk incredibly sharply, with areas undergoing conversion to plantations or grazing land (in Madeira, the Azores and UK) or housing (in South Africa).

Research at the Royal Botanic Garden Edinburgh has shown that the ragged specklebelly is part of a cryptic complex of closely related lichens, which cannot be distinguished from one another by their physical form, only by studying their DNA. Although these mysterious beings have not been formally assessed on a global level – few lichens have – even if all members of the complex were combined they would still be rare enough to qualify as threatened under the IUCN's globally recognised criteria.

> *A true rainforest organism – and right at home in Scotland.*

Specimen notes | The Benmore population was established in 2019 as a conservation translocation from an unprotected site in Scotland's Atlantic temperate rainforest.

Location | Benmore.

Conservation status | VU

Adelmeria isarogensis

As far as is known, *Adelmeria isarogensis* (Zingiberaceae – ginger family) is found only in the Bicol Region of Luzon, the largest island in the Philippines. The species has been recorded on all three of the highest mountains in the Region: Mayon Volcano (2,463 metres), Mount Isarog (1,951 metres) and Mount Malinao (1,548 metres).

The first collection was made on Mayon Volcano in June 1953, but the species is named for Mount Isarog, which is considered by many to be the site of the last intact tropical forests in the Bicol Region.

When is a pinecone not a pinecone?

These enormous herbs form clumps up to three metres tall, and carry their congested inflorescences (flowering heads) – which bear a remarkable resemblance to pinecones – at the end of a leafy shoot. Found in montane forests, they are happiest in inaccessible ravines, making them difficult to collect in the field.

In the past, the various species of *Adelmeria* were all lumped under the large, 'dustbin' ginger genus *Alpinia.* However, recent genetic and morphological studies by Rudolph Valentino A. Docot of the University of Santo Tomas, Philippines, supervised by Royal Botanic Garden Edinburgh research fellow Axel Dalberg Poulsen, have confirmed that *Adelmeria* is a coherent evolutionary grouping in its own right. In the process they named four species new to science – of which *A. isarogensis* was one.

Of the three populations of *A. isarogensis* so far identified, that on Mayon Volcano is at risk of being destroyed by volcanic activity, while that on Mount Malinao is threatened by the conversion of its forest habitat to agricultural land. The population on Mount Isarog, at least, is so far stable and the mountain is designated a protected area.

Specimen notes | Grown from a cutting collected during a Royal Botanic Garden Edinburgh and Philippines National Herbarium Expedition to Mount Isarog in 1997.

Location | Edinburgh (Glasshouses).

Conservation status |

Coptis teeta

Coptis teeta (Ranunculaceae – buttercup family) is a delicate beauty hidden in the undergrowth of tropical forests in Arunchal Pradesh and north-west Yunnan, with 90 per cent of the population confined to the former. Known as 云南黄连 (*yun nan huang lian*; meaning 'Yunnan goldthread') in China, and *mamira* or *mishmi* in India, it has highly divided, fern-like leaves and small, greenish-yellow flowers with spoon-shaped petals.

The rhizome (underground stem) of Yunnan goldthread is used in Chinese traditional medicine as an antibacterial and anti-inflammatory ingredient, treating fever, headaches and stomach complaints. Increasing demand for the rhizomes – sold in India under the name *mishmi teeta* and in China as *yun lian* – has led to unregulated commercial collection which, combined with forest degradation from slash-and-burn agriculture and road construction, has resulted in populations declining by 60 per cent over just a decade. With reportedly very specific habitat requirements, high levels of male sterility, low reproductive success rates, inadequate seed dispersal, and little genetic variability, the goldthread has little likelihood of recovering from these threats.

Specimen notes | Collected in Yunnan, China, by the Gaoligong Shan Biotic Survey Expedition, a collaboration between the Royal Botanic Garden Edinburgh, Kunming Institute of Botany and the California Academy of Sciences, USA, in 1997.

Location | Edinburgh (not on public display).

Conservation status | EN

However, there is some positive news: in India, the goldthread's populations now lie within a protected area. In Yunnan, a programme of small-scale cultivation within a sustainable agroforestry system, undertaken by the Lisu ethnic minority people, seems to be sufficient to provide income for local people whilst also protecting the species and its habitat.

The Royal Botanic Garden Edinburgh has a long history of work within, and collaboration with, China, particularly in Yunnan. Since the early 1980s we have taken part in multiple collaborative expeditions to Yunnan with our partner institute, Kunming Institute of Botany, Chinese Academy of Sciences. Several of these visited the Gaoligong Shan range – a United Nations Educational, Scientific and Cultural Organization (UNESCO) Biosphere Reserve within the Hengduan Mountains biodiversity hotspot, and from which our Yunnan goldthread plant originates. In 2001 we founded a joint field station with the Kunming Institute of Botany on the Yulong Xue Shan (Jade Dragon Snow Mountain).

> *Got a fever or headache? Yunnan goldthread is widely used as a traditional medicine in China and India.*

Sorbus pseudomeinichii

Sorbus pseudomeinichii (Rosaceae – rose family), the Catacol whitebeam, is an extremely rare tree: only two individuals are known in the wild, in Glen Catacol on Scotland's island of Arran.

The first tree was found here in June 1949, by Scottish ecologist Donald McVean (1926–2017), although at the time it was not recognised as anything special and misidentified as *S. aucuparia*, the common rowan.

Half a century later, Royal Botanic Garden Edinburgh botanist Phil Lusby saw McVean's specimen, and knew that this was no ordinary rowan. The location was given broadly as Glen Catacol, meaning that relocating the plant would be challenging. Lusby later chanced upon it in the early 2000s during unrelated fieldwork in Arran. In fact, Lusby says he had been leaning on the tree for some time before realising what it was! It was named as a distinct species by *Sorbus* PhD student Ashley Robertson in 2006. A second tree was discovered in 2019.

One of the rarest trees in the world.

It is now thought that the Catacol whitebeam is a complex hybrid, resulting from an initial cross between rowan and rock whitebeam (*S. rupicola*), followed by two generations of backcrossing to rowan. The species, along with its two rare precursor hybrids (*S. arranensis* and *S. pseudofennica*), is found only on Arran. All three are maintained through agamospermy – the production of seeds without fertilisation, which then germinate into clones of the parent plant.

Sorbus arranensis (Arran whitebeam) is endangered and *S. pseudofennica* (Arran service-tree) is, like the Catacol whitebeam, critically endangered.

The UK is a centre of diversity for *Sorbus*, a group in which unusual genetic phenomena are common. Combined with the ability to reproduce without fertilisation, this has led to the creation of multiple distinct, stable species – and a great deal of controversy among botanists! Here, we stick with the generic name *Sorbus*, as used in the IUCN Red List and World Flora Online.

The main threat to the Catacol whitebeam in the wild is the risk of a landslips caused by erosion, with high browsing pressure from sheep and red deer preventing any regeneration. However, Royal Botanic Garden Edinburgh horticulturists have propagated new trees from seed and by grafting with rowan rootstocks. Some of these can now be seen growing at Edinburgh and Benmore.

Specimen notes | All three rare Arran *Sorbus* species have been propagated from seed and cuttings collected in the wild.

Location | Edinburgh (Rock Garden, Experimental Garden, East Gate); Benmore.

Conservation status |

Zingiber vinosum

Zingiber vinosum (Zingiberaceae) is a striking species of ginger from the lowland tropical rainforests of Borneo. The first person to spot that it was unlike any other species known to science was Rosemary Margaret Smith (1933–2004), a botanist, illustrator and ginger specialist working at the Royal Botanic Garden Edinburgh, in 1988. However, it was not formally named until 1997 by Ida Theilade, a botanist and conservationist at the University of Copenhagen, and John Mood of Waimea Arboretum and Botanical Garden, Hawaii, who had also collected the species.

Borneo is one of the world's biodiversity hotspots and exceptionally rich in gingers, with over 250 species described so far, in 19 different genera, four of which are found nowhere else. *Zingiber vinosum* is unique to three sites in the Malaysian state of Sabah. It is named *vinosum* (wine-like) for its leaves' deep burgundy colour.

Borneo's forest species are under continuous threat from logging and conversion, and those inhabited by *Z. vinosum* are no exception: while the subpopulations in Danum Valley and Sepilok Forest Reserve are protected, most of the forest at the third location has already been converted to plantations. *Ex-situ* conservation may be essential to its survival, and so far Botanic Gardens Conservation International reports that it is being grown at three botanic gardens – one of which is the Royal Botanic Garden Edinburgh.

In fact, *Z. vinosum* has been growing in Edinburgh since before it was even scientifically described. The Garden's George Argent (1941–2019), affectionately nicknamed 'the Indiana Jones of botany', collected a plant in Sabah in 1985 and grew it on in the Rock House, where it stubbornly refused to flower for many years.

> *A wine-coloured rarity from one of the world's ginger hotspots.*

Specimen notes | Collected in 1985 in Danum Valley, Sabah, Malaysia by George Argent.

Location | Edinburgh (Glasshouses).

Conservation status | EN

Lathyrus belinensis

The Belin pea, *Lathyrus belinensis* (Fabaceae), is restricted to an extremely small area in the thin strip of Mediterranean habitat that runs around the south coast of Turkey. The area is somewhat of a 'pea hotspot': since its discovery, at least three more species of *Lathyrus* have been found in Turkey – one of them as recently as 2021, which at time of writing had not yet been given a scientific name.

A close relative of the garden sweet pea (*Lathyrus odoratus*), the Belin pea was itself only formally described in 1987, by renowned legume specialist and champion of crop wild relatives Nigel Maxted, along with David Goyder of the Royal Botanic Gardens, Kew.

> *A little-known beauty and close cousin of the garden sweet pea.*

The Belin pea's exquisite bi-coloured flowers have an apricot banner, traced with darker orange lines, and golden lower petals. Its scent is not quite as powerful as that of the true sweet pea, but stronger than most other species of *Lathyrus*, making it a good candidate for the garden. A fast-growing annual species, it is well adapted to its Mediterranean climate. A tough coat protects the seeds against intense sun and drought. They can remain dormant for many years, but are quick to germinate when conditions are right.

We do not know how many times the Belin pea has been introduced into cultivation, but nursery-grown seed is readily available to buy, despite how rare it is in the wild. The main threats to the species are the risk of development in the small area where it survives, and climate change. *Ex-situ* collections such as those at the Royal Botanic Garden Edinburgh help ensure the future of the species.

Specimen notes | Cultivated from stock collected in 1973 and donated to the Royal Botanic Garden Edinburgh in the early 2000s. An annual species, it is regrown from seed and may be seen in a different location every year.

Location | Edinburgh.

Conservation status | CR

Pandanus pristis

Pandanus pristis (Pandanaceae) is one of the screw pines, or screw palms: 'screw' for the spiralling pattern of leaf scars encircling their stems, 'pine' for the pineapple-like fruits, and 'palm' because the whole plant resembles a palm, though they are not at all closely related. There are around 750 species of screw palm growing across the tropics and subtropics of Africa and Asia.

Pandanus pristis is found only in the dry forests of Madagascar, an extraordinarily biodiverse hotspot: around 95 per cent of the island's reptiles, 89 per cent of plants and 92 per cent of mammals exist nowhere else on the planet.

Pandanus pristis was first named as new to science by Benjamin Clemens Masterman Stone (1933–1994) in the journal of the Paris Musée National d'Histoire Naturelle, *Adansonia*, in 1971. Stone, born in Shanghai, was a prolific botanist and skilled botanical illustrator who founded the Guam Herbarium, wrote the *Flora of Guam*, started the journal *Micronesia* (which is still published today), and authored more than 300 scientific papers.

Stone identified the distinctive new species from a plant in Munich Botanic Garden, which flowered in 1970. He chose the epithet *pristis* from the scientific name for the sawfish, which itself comes from the Greek for saw, as the plant's leaves resemble the fish's saw-shaped rostrum (bill).

The plant named after a fish!

Pandanus pristis occurs within an area of only 876 square kilometres, within which it actually occupies just 24 square kilometres. The majority of individuals are isolated in four subpopulations – Andrafiamena, Andavokoera, Ankarana and Loky-Manambato – fortunately all within protected areas. Nonetheless, the number of plants is still decreasing.

The main threat to *P. pristis* is decreasing habitat quantity and quality due to ongoing mining, grazing, charcoal production, forest exploitation and slash-and-burn deforestation. The work of botanic gardens can help mitigate some of these factors: the Royal Botanic Garden Edinburgh has a growing Madagascar programme, focusing on mediating the complex interactions between forest, savanna, fire, climate change and human livelihoods.

Specimen notes | Received as a cutting in 1979 from the Natural History Museum, London, having been collected in Fort Dauphin, Toliara, Madagascar.

Location | Edinburgh (Glasshouses).

Conservation status | EN

Herbertus borealis

Herbertus borealis (Herbertaceae), the northern prongwort, is a liverwort totally unique to Scotland. It is found only on Beinn Eighe in Wester Ross – where it is fairly abundant on the plateau – and Slioch, immediately to the north.

The northern prongwort is one of four bryophyte species known only from Scotland, and certainly the most charismatic. It is a handsome and distinctive plant, often a bright orange-brown colour, with pointed leaf lobes that are neatly swept over to one side. Like Lindenberg's featherwort, it grows in the highly specialised oceanic-montane liverwort-rich heath community, which depends on the more-or-less constantly wet climate of Scotland's north-west uplands for its continued existence.

> *A unique Scottish liverwort with connections to the Himalaya.*

The northern prongwort was previously thought to occur also in Norway, but genetic evidence now shows that the Norwegian populations belong to an entirely different species, *H. norenus* (Viking prongwort), which is also found in Shetland. The northern prongwort's closest (though far-flung!) living relative may in fact be *H. delavayi* (Delavay's prongwort) from the Sino-Himalaya.

Threats to the northern prongwort include muirburn or wildfire, as well as the potential for climate change to disrupt the weather patterns essential for oceanic-montane liverwort-rich heath to persist. Its very small range, limited to two near-adjacent sites, increases the risk of extinction.

One of those sites, Beinn Eighe, became the UK's first National Nature Reserve in 1951, and in 2019 it also became the first Genetic Conservation Area. The plateau is now managed by NatureScot to protect the specific genetic type of the area's totemic Scots pines (*Pinus sylvestris*), allowing them to evolve and adapt to the pressures of climate change. This should also benefit much smaller but equally precious species like the northern prongwort.

Specimen notes | Herbarium specimens dating back to 1958. This species is not yet held in the Living Collection but is subject to intensive study by the Royal Botanic Garden Edinburgh's cryptogam team in the field.

Location | Edinburgh (Herbarium).

Conservation status | VU

Abutilon menziesii

Found only in Hawaii, *Abutilon menziesii* (Malvaceae – mallow family) has pretty, heart-shaped leaves covered in silver, velvety hairs, and bears very attractive, red, *Hibiscus*-like flowers which droop coyly downwards, often hidden by the foliage. The blossoms, like those of *Hibiscus*, are traditionally used for lei making, while a juice squeezed from the flowers is taken as a mild laxative.

Known locally as *ko'oloa'ula*, and further afield as red *ilima*, it is one of four *Abutilon* species from Hawaii, of which three are endemic (found nowhere else) and critically endangered. *Ko'oloa'ula* can now be seen planted across the archipelago – its drought-tolerance makes it a good choice for gardens – but is found in the wild at just 10 sites on the islands of Hawaii, Molokai, Lana'i and O'ahu. The entire population comprises only 450–500 individuals.

Inhabiting dry forest – a rare and threatened habitat globally – *ko'oloa'ula* faces multiple threats including grazing, competition from introduced invasive plants, invertebrate pests, fire, development and agriculture. The species' existing habitats are already highly degraded and often dominated by invasive species. When *ko'oloa'ula* was last assessed in 2003, it was expected to decline in numbers by 80 per cent over the following decade: an up-to-date assessment is urgently needed to confirm whether the worst has happened.

> *The entire wild population of ko'oloa'ula numbers only 500 individuals.*

A Habitat Conservation Plan was actioned for one *ko'oloa'ula* population, at Kapolei, between 1996 and 2021. Despite being one of the most intensive species-focused conservation projects in Hawaii, it met with only limited success. Natural recruitment of *ko'oloa'ula* seedlings was very low, due to factors including variable climate, human land use and development, and seeds being eaten by introduced species such as deer. Further management action is needed to ensure the species' survival in the wild.

Specimen notes | Grown from seed produced via controlled pollination, received in 1992 from the Jardin du Conservatoire Botanique National de Brest. A second plant was grown from seed of the original collection in 2010, but this did not survive.

Location | Edinburgh (not on public display).

Conservation status | CR

Araucaria muelleri

Sometimes known as the king araucaria, the conifer *Araucaria muelleri* (Araucariaceae) is found in the wild only in the South Pacific archipelago of New Caledonia, 750 miles off the east coast of Australia. New Caledonia is the world's smallest biodiversity hotspot: seven per cent of the world's conifers are unique to these islands, and it is home to 14 of the world's 20 *Araucaria* species.

Araucaria muelleri inhabits just a few sites in the southernmost part of New Caledonia's largest island, Grand Terre. It is often found in areas of *maquis minier* – a specialised form of vegetation characterised by evergreen, leathery-leaved shrubs with a canopy of emergent trees. *Maquis minier* soils are often ultramafic – of low fertility, but a globally important source of nickel – and the king araucaria is used as an indicator of nickel-rich soils.

Threatened for the very ground on which it grows: soils rich in nickel, in great demand for items such as electric cars.

The most imminent threat to the species is fire, exacerbated by climate-change-induced droughts. Open-cast nickel mining, which is likely to accelerate with the increased popularity of electric cars, comes a close second.

King araucaria trees grow up to 25 metres tall with an open, candelabra-like crown. Their leaves, at up to 3.5 centimetres long, are the largest of any New Caledonian *Araucaria*. Separate male and female cones are produced, with the brownish male pollen-bearing cones drooping from the tips of branches and the round female seed cones growing on very short branches.

In 2016, scientists at the Royal Botanic Garden Edinburgh figured out that many trees previously ascribed to *A. muelleri* were in fact an undescribed species, now named *A. goroensis*, making the king araucaria even rarer than we thought. Our understanding of biodiversity never stops growing!

Specimen notes | Three survivors remain from a batch of seedlings collected in 2002 by a Royal Botanic Garden Edinburgh expedition to New Caledonia.

Location | Edinburgh (not on public display).

Conservation status | EN

Camellia azalea

An evergreen shrub with glossy green leaves and beautiful red flowers, *Camellia azalea* (Theaceae – tea family) is understandably in demand as an ornamental. With an exceptionally long blooming period from May right through to winter, it is aptly known as the rose of winter. Confusingly, it is not an azalea, which is used as a common name for some members of the genus *Rhododendron*!

Found only in China, the rose of winter exists at a single location: Ehuangzhang Nature Reserve in Guangdong. Here, there is a continuing decline in range, quality and extent of habitat, and in the number of mature individuals. At last count, the population comprised around 1,000 individuals, but their limited genetic diversity makes the effective population size much smaller.

Fruit set, seed production and seed germination all appear to be constrained in the wild population. The species relies upon cross-fertilisation by bees and butterflies, yet pollinator visits are few. Artificial pollination may prove necessary to increase seed set and regeneration in the wild.

The species faces multiple threats, including human disturbance, damming of the rivers alongside which it likes to grow, and continuing collection from the wild for the horticultural trade. Established in 2000, the Ehuangzhang Nature Reserve provides some protection, but the incentive to collect plants remains high as cultivated supplies of *Camellia azalea* are still insufficient to meet demand. Propagation techniques have been developed in private nurseries and, through this, 10,000 grafted plants have been purchased by the nature reserve and distributed among local people in an attempt to reduce illegal collection.

In the wild, this species is confined to a single nature reserve in southern China.

Specimen notes | Grown from seed supplied by Kunming Institute of Botany from their wild-origin plant, received at the Royal Botanic Garden Edinburgh in 2018.

Location | Edinburgh; Logan (not on display).

Conservation status | CR

Lathyrus odoratus

It comes as no surprise that *Lathyrus odoratus*, the sweet pea, is a regular entry in the UK public's top five favourite plants. Clearly recognisable to plant lovers everywhere, it is hugely popular in gardens and as a cut flower, with gorgeous blooms and a distinctive heady scent. In fact, it is one of only a handful (around five) of the 160 species of *Lathyrus* to be strongly scented.

Although anecdotally said to have been grown by the Romans, it is first known for certain to have been introduced to northern climes by the Sicilian naturalist-monk, Francesco Cupani (1657–1710), in 1699. Cupani, whose name is commemorated in a major group of sweet pea varieties, sent seed to both English cleric and plantsman Robert Uvedale (1642–1722) and Dutch botanist Caspar Commelin (1668–1731) in Amsterdam.

> *Rumoured to have been cultivated since Roman times.*

There are well over 3,000 registered cultivars and varieties of sweet pea, with flowers ranging from the neat, smooth-edged petals of the wild type to large, ostentatious frilled ones. They come in an incredible array of colours, too – although no one has yet managed to breed a yellow one! The wild variety has two-tone flowers, with violet lower elements and a maroon banner.

Now cultivated in temperate and warm subtropical areas around the globe, in the wild the sweet pea is critically endangered, its small and fragmented populations threatened mainly by over-collection of seed.

Although related to broad beans, lentils, and edible peas – which were recently reclassified alongside their ornamental cousin in the genus *Lathyrus* – the seeds of the sweet pea contain a toxin which make them unsuitable for eating. Nonetheless, they are functional as well as beautiful: all species of *Lathyrus* are nitrogen fixers, making atmospheric nitrogen available to other plants in the soil via bacteria housed in specialised root nodules. Using sweet peas in agriculture as a companion or rotation crop can drastically reduce the need for polluting artificial nitrogen fertilisers, the production of which has a huge carbon cost. Protecting peas can be positive in more ways than one!

Specimen notes | New sweet pea plants are cultivated each year by the horticulture students at the Royal Botanic Garden Edinburgh.

Location | Edinburgh.

Conservation status | CR

Taxus chinensis

In the 1960s, the bark of certain yew trees was discovered, during a mass botanical drug screening programme by the US National Cancer Institute, to contain small amounts of the substance paclitaxel – often marketed under the brand name Taxol – a potent chemotherapy drug now used to treat breast, ovarian and lung cancers, and AIDS-related Kaposi's sarcoma.

Taxus chinensis (the Chinese yew; Taxaceae – yew family), along with other yew species, was later found to contain chemical precursors of paclitaxel in its bark and leaves. Extracting these is a more economical way of producing Taxol than harvesting the active compound itself, and needn't kill the tree – if it is done with care.

Native to China, where it is called 红豆杉, *hong dou shan*, and Vietnam, where it is known as *thông đỏ bắc*, *T. chinensis* is a slow-growing and long-lived conifer which can easily survive to 1,000 years old. In addition to its modern use, traditionally *T. chinensis* wood is used in construction, furniture-making, wood-carving and turning. Extracts of the roots, wood, bark and leaves are used in traditional Chinese medicine, as

Specimen notes | Introduced to the Royal Botanic Garden Edinburgh on many occasions, but only one tree survives today, a Champion Tree obtained from Hillier and Sons' nursery in 1931.

Location | Edinburgh (South Side).

Conservation status | EN

is an oil extracted from the seeds. Almost all parts of the plant are poisonous.

Since the discovery of Taxol, widespread and indiscriminate stripping of the bark and foliage has destroyed many mature trees. With little natural regeneration happening, the population is shrinking rapidly.

> *Yews are of great medical importance as the source of powerful anti-cancer drug, Taxol.*

The Chinese yew is now listed on CITES (the Convention on International Trade in Endangered Species of Wild Fauna and Flora, or the Washington Convention) Appendix II, which heavily regulates international trade in the species. In China, harvesting the wild plants in all forms was banned in 2003, and in Vietnam its exploitation for commercial purposes is restricted.

Attempts are now being made to grow the Chinese yew in cultivation to meet demand for paclitaxel without destroying wild populations – and several plantations have been established in China. However, due to the slow-growing nature of the plants, exploitation of wild trees is likely to continue for some time.

Paphiopedilum lawrenceanum

Extremely rare in the wild, and confined to Mount Kinabalu on the island of Borneo, *Paphiopedilum lawrenceanum* (Lawrence's slipper orchid; Orchidaceae – orchid family) is unusual among orchids for growing on the ground, rooted in the leaf litter covering limestone rocks – most orchids prefer to grow as epiphytes (air plants) on other plants.

This is a small orchid, with leaves mottled dark and yellow-green above, pale green below, bearing its striking flowers singly on stems up to 30 centimetres in length. Their dorsal sepal is striped maroon and white, the labellum (the large, modified petal at the base of the flower) is maroon, and the rest of the tepals are greenish, edged with black spots. The species was named by western scientists for Sir Trevor Lawrence (1831–1913), president of the Royal Horticultural Society.

Fewer than 50 mature individuals now exist in the wild, their numbers having been slashed in recent decades for many reasons, including ruthless collection for both regional and international trade, copper mining on Mount Kinabalu, and habitat degradation through logging and human disturbance.

All *Paphiopedilum* species are listed on Appendix I – for species most at risk – of CITES, and this slipper orchid also occurs within a protected area. However, illegal collection continues and the species remains highly threatened. Species-based management and conservation will be essential to protect the remaining few individuals on Mount Kinabalu.

> *Despite prohibitions on trade, this orchid is so desirable that collection from the wild continues.*

Specimen notes | Cultivated plants received from the Royal Botanic Gardens, Kew in 1987. Kew in turn received them from Missouri Botanical Garden, USA.

Location | Edinburgh (Glasshouses).

Conservation status | CR

Paphiopedilum parishii

Known in Myanmar as *zawgyi-moteseik*, and in the UK as Parish's slipper orchid, this rare orchid grows in China, Myanmar, Thailand and Laos. Although this sounds like a large range, it occurs at just five known locations within this area, covering a total of only 150 square kilometres.

This slow-growing species is found in the monsoon zone – warm and very wet in summer – growing on tree trunks or rocks in broad-leaved forest, preferring deeply shaded east-facing slopes. Each plant bears up to 10 flowers on a single flower spike, with narrow, twisted dark red tepals and a white dorsal sepal striped with green. The 'Parish' name-checked in the species' epithet is Charles Samuel Pollock Parish (1822–1897), an English botanist specialising in the flora of Myanmar.

In 2014, Chinese scientists reported the discovery of a previously unknown method of self-pollination in *Paphiopedilum parishii*: the pollen-containing anthers become liquified and at the same time the flower bends to allow this liquid droplet to slide down onto the stigma, where the pollen germinates to fertilise the ovules and produce seed. This phenomenon occurs even before the flower is fully open, and may be an adaptation to a scarcity of pollinating insects in the extremely shady and humid forests where it grows.

Its bizarre self-pollination mechanism is thought to be unmatched in the plant kingdom.

Threats to the continued existence of this unusual species include climate change and potential drought, logging, fire, deforestation and habitat destruction, trampling, and collection for regional and international horticultural trade.

Like *P. lawrenceanum*, *P. parishii* is listed on CITES Appendix I. *Ex-situ* conservation at gardens such as the Royal Botanic Garden Edinburgh is also helping ensure these stunning plants survive for future generations.

Specimen notes | Cultivated plants received from the Royal Botanic Gardens, Kew in 1987. Kew in turn received them from Missouri Botanical Garden, USA.

Location | Edinburgh (Glasshouses).

Conservation status | EN

Streptocarpus thysanotus

Streptocarpus thysanotus (Gesneriaceae – African violet family) is known in the wild from only a single location in the Uluguru Mountains of Tanzania. Occasionally cultivated as an ornamental, *S. thysanotus* is rather a robust member of the genus *Streptocarpus* (Cape primroses), reaching heights of 75 centimetres, but has relatively tiny flowers just a centimetre or so across.

Streptocarpus thysanotus was first collected in lowland moist forest in the early 1970s by the Royal Botanic Garden Edinburgh's Brian Laurence 'Bill' Burtt (1913–2008) and Hungarian botanist Tamás Pócs who, at the age of 88, was still publishing as this book went to press! Burtt and Pócs' specimen, which had no flowers, came to the Royal Botanic Garden Edinburgh, where it was not thought to be anything new.

> *It took until four years after collection for this plant to flower, and scientists to realise it was a new species!*

When it eventually flowered after being propagated from seed, the plant was clearly different from all other *Streptocarpus* recorded from the area. In 1975, Burtt was able to describe and formally name the species, working with Olive Mary Hilliard. At that time Burtt and Hilliard comprised the Royal Botanic Garden Edinburgh's Gesneriaceae crack team! First working together in the 1960s, they married in 2004 after a long career together making the Royal Botanic Garden Edinburgh a centre of Gesneriaceae research.

In the wild, *S. thysanotus* continues to decline, mainly due to a reduction in habitat extent and quality caused by human activity. Further research is needed to find out more about the species' requirements in order to protect it from extinction and monitor the effect of any conservation actions. It is thought to be held at only two botanic gardens in the world, of which the Royal Botanic Garden Edinburgh is one.

Specimen notes | Seed collected in Tanzania has been propagated on through 10 generations to produce the plants growing at the Royal Botanic Garden Edinburgh today.

Location | Edinburgh (Glasshouses).

Conservation status |

Pelargonium insularis

Pelargonium insularis (Geraniaceae – geranium family) is found exclusively on the island of Samha in the Soqotra archipelago, Yemen. The first western scientist to see it was the Royal Botanic Garden Edinburgh's Tony Miller, in 1999 – and his collection remains the first, and only, formal record of *Pelargonium* in Soqotra.

The plant grows on the steep cliffs of a north-facing limestone escarpment. A perennial with a thick, succulent stem, it has rounded leaves, and produces pale pink clusters of flowers. Originally found as a single plant, the entire population of this species is now estimated at fewer than 50 individuals.

The limestone escarpment cliffs have been designated a Natural Sanctuary, but this does not mean the species is out of danger. The microclimate created by the cliffs, of frequent low cloud providing a moist refuge in this otherwise desert island, is likely to disappear due to climate change, which is already causing reductions in the region's rainfall. A second threat is from browsing livestock: although traditionally the island's sheep and goats have been herded away from the limestone plateau in periods of drought, changes in livestock management may result in overgrazing of this fragile ecosystem.

The only Pelargonium known from the whole Soqotra archipelago.

Finding itself in such a precarious situation in the wild, *ex-situ* conservation is increasingly important for *P. insularis*. At the Royal Botanic Garden Edinburgh, we continue to propagate the species through both seed and cuttings, helping ensure the species' long-term future.

Specimen notes | Collected on Samha by Tony Miller in 1999. The original plant successfully set seed, from which new plants were propagated in 2000; further seed-grown plants were propagated in 2020.

Location | Edinburgh (not on public display).

Conservation status | CR

Pelargonium cotyledonis

Found only on the highly biodiverse South Atlantic island of St Helena, *Pelargonium cotyledonis* is sometimes known as 'old father live forever', because individual plants can be extremely long-lived. However, the species as a whole may not be in such great shape.

With a thick, succulent stem and pure white flowers, old father live forever grows on cliffs and escarpments on the eastern and southern coasts of the island, in a population of around 1,600 individuals. The population is divided into small colonies of plants, many of these confined to a single rocky outcrop.

An exciting example of evolution in action.

Looking across the island, the plants exhibit some diversity in form: some populations have glossy green, rounded leaves; in others the leaves are softer green and more oval. In a study by Alastair Maclaren, BSc student at the Royal Botanic Garden Edinburgh and Scotland's Rural College, plants from the east of St Helena were shown to differ genetically and morphologically from those in the west – an exciting example of evolutionary divergence within species on an island.

Threats to the 'old father' include grazing (goats, which were a threat in the past, have been largely eradicated from the island, but grazing by rabbits continues to limit seedling establishment), attack by mealy bugs, which can persist on the roots, and competition from invasive shrubs and tussock grasses.

Fortunately, many parts of the species' range are protected in National Conservation Areas. As well as this *in-situ* protection, and *ex-situ* conservation in botanic gardens, this unusual species is widely cultivated as a pot plant.

Specimen notes | Seed and cuttings obtained from Cambridge University Botanic Garden in 1957, a plant from Dundee University Botanic Garden in 1984, and plants from the Chelsea Physic Garden in 2000. Seed from the 1957 accession was successfully propagated at the Royal Botanic Garden Edinburgh in 2011 and 2020. Seed is also stored in our seed bank.

Location | Edinburgh (not on public display).

Conservation status |

Agave cupreata

Agave cupreata (Agavaceae) – known as *maguey papalote* or the dwarf cowhorn agave – is found exclusively on the mountain slopes of the Rio Balsas basin in Mexico, in the states of Michoacán and Guerrero.

It is one of around 200 species of *Agave* scattered across central and South America, used to make everything from sweeteners to didgeridoos. Perhaps their most famous use, though, is in the production of the spirits *mezcal* and *tequila*.

While the leaves of the dwarf cowhorn agave can reach 40–80 centimetres in length, it produces a flowering stalk (*quiote*) 10 times that size. The *quiote* bears yellow, funnel-shaped flowers, which are pollinated by bats. The species is monocarpic – it flowers once before dying – although it may live for many years before reaching flowering age.

Both *mezcal* and *tequila* are made by roasting the hearts – or *piñas* – of the plant, formed from the bases of the leaves. Just prior to flowering, the *piñas* become enriched with sugars. *Mezcal* producers cut the emerging *quiote* to concentrate the sugars in the *piña*, which is then harvested, roasted, mashed and fermented. Removing the *quiote* prevents the plant from reaching its once-in-a-lifetime chance to set seed, limiting natural reproduction.

The dwarf cowhorn agave is now one of the most widely used agaves for *mezcal* production where it occurs. *Agave tequilana* (blue agave) was once favoured, but as its numbers declined, trade shifted to the dwarf cowhorn. Many wild populations of dwarf cowhorn agave have now been destroyed and replaced with commercial plantations of the same species. It is estimated that over 50 per cent of wild individuals have now been lost.

According to the most recent conservation assessment, in 2018, little protection is in place for the dwarf cowhorn agave at present. Some populations do occur within a protected area and, in Chilapa region, *mezcaleros* have begun to leave some larger plants to flower and produce seed. However, more comprehensive management plans including harvesting quotas are probably needed to protect the species.

> *A boom and bust species, Agave cupreata puts everything it has into one spectacular flowering season, then dies.*

Specimen notes | Grown from seed obtained from a commercial nursery in 2012.

Location | Edinburgh (Glasshouses).

Conservation status | EN

Etlingera hyalina

Etlingera hyalina (Zingiberaceae), the ghost ginger, is relatively new to science, being described in 2012 by Axel Dalberg Poulsen, *Etlingera* expert and research fellow at the Royal Botanic Garden Edinburgh. Unique to Sulawesi, Indonesia, it grows in loose clumps up to 2.5 metres tall – sometimes held up to 60 centimetres above the ground on stilt roots where the soils are waterlogged.

The ghost ginger occurs in primary evergreen forest, a habitat which is estimated to be declining in both quality and extent. Logging and land conversion already taking place in nearby forests has the potential to spread to the range of the ghost ginger, which is not thought to be subject to any form of protection.

> *Scientists first spotted this species by chance, as they cleared a site to make camp!*

The species has been found only twice, both at the same location – Gunung Hek – and both during joint expeditions by the Royal Botanic Garden Edinburgh and the Indonesian Institute of Sciences. The first plant was discovered in 2004, when clearing a space to camp for the night during the expedition. The second time the species was spotted, in 2008, it was fruiting, so seeds were collected and propagated at the Royal Botanic Garden Edinburgh, where they later flowered.

The epithet *hyalina*, meaning 'glassy' or 'translucent', is derived from the pale pinkish-white, translucent bracts (modified leaves supporting and protecting the developing flowers), through which the pink flowers can be seen. The flower itself hardly extends beyond these covering bracts. The spooky appearance this creates earned it the nickname 'ghost ginger', which was used by botanists until the species was formally given its scientific name.

Specimen notes | Grown from seed collected by Royal Botanic Garden Edinburgh PhD student Daniel Thomas on a joint expedition with the Indonesian Institute of Sciences in 2008.

Location | Edinburgh (Glasshouses).

Conservation status | EN

Pinus maximartinezii

Known variously as *maxipiñon*, *pino azul*, *piñon real*, big-cone pinyon and Martinez pinyon, *Pinus maximartinezii* (Pinaceae – pine family) is considered to be one of the rarest conifers on Earth. The species is found in just two locations in central Mexico, the second of which was only discovered in 2010.

The *maxipiñon* was described formally in 1964, but has been well known to local people for generations as an important source of pine nuts. Indeed, it is said to produce the largest and most nutritious seed of all the pines, and these form a staple part of the local diet.

The origin of this species is somewhat controversial – it may have come about through a natural hybridisation of other pine species, or even through intentional cross-breeding by humans in an attempt to create larger pine nuts. DNA evidence suggests that the *maxipiñon* went through a 'genetic bottleneck' – indicating a previous period of low population size – between 400 and 1,000 years ago. The population has again declined considerably over the past century, through a devastating combination of overharvesting of seeds, grazing by cattle, and fire.

The main threat to the species is considered to be cattle grazing, which increased significantly around 50 years ago. At that time, large areas of land were cleared for cattle ranching by burning the vegetation, killing the trees. Grazing and trampling by the cattle themselves then caused erosion of the shallow, rocky soils, destroying suitable sites for any future seed germination and preventing seedling establishment.

Pine nut harvesting can be sustainable if fire and grazing are managed. The land on which the remaining *maxipiñon* trees grow is owned by local people, who have an interest in sustainable production. However, they also need to graze their cattle on the land, creating an uneasy conflict of interest. Seeds of the *maxipiñon* have been sent to multiple *ex-situ* conservation programmes, including at the Royal Botanic Garden Edinburgh, which may be crucial to the species' survival.

The source of the world's largest, most nutritious pine nuts.

Specimen notes | Seed collected in 1991 in Zacatecas, Mexico.

Location | Seed held in the Edinburgh seed bank. Also planted at Ard-na-Sidhe Country House, Republic of Ireland, by our International Conifer Conservation Programme as part of a network of conifer safe sites.

Conservation status | EN

Begonia samhaensis

Begonia samhaensis (Begoniaceae – begonia family) is named for the island of Samha in the Indian Ocean archipelago of Soqotra. Like its sister species, *B. socotrana* – the only other species of *Begonia* in the archipelago – it seems to be a winter-flowering species. With begonias being such popular ornamentals, this feature is in great demand for breeding and makes *B. samhaensis* potentially of enormous value to horticulture – and therefore very vulnerable in the wild.

Begonia samhaensis was first spotted by the Royal Botanic Garden Edinburgh's Vanessa Plana during an expedition in 1996, where a single plant was seen on cliffs near the summit of the island. In 1999, a small population of *B. samhaensis* was discovered at the very summit of Samha, containing about 30 plants occupying the area of a single large limestone block measuring about 50 square metres – roughly one fifth the size of a tennis court.

A rare and beautiful winter-flowering Begonia.

Samha's climate is characterised by a long, hot, dry season between monsoon rains, and the persistence of *B. samhaensis* is attributed to the presence of low clouds which skim the summit and deposit meagre amounts of moisture on the limestone block. The plants can only survive in the nooks and crannies of the rock, out of reach of browsing goats. As Royal Botanic Garden Edinburgh

Begonia expert Mark Hughes says with characteristic understatement in his 2002 PhD thesis, "It is in fact quite surprising *B. samhaensis* is not extinct".

With more than 2,000 species of all shapes and sizes – many of them restricted to a single site – *Begonia* is one of the world's largest flowering plant genera. A key focus of research at the Royal Botanic Garden Edinburgh, it can be used to model everything from the genetics of leaf form to the evolutionary radiation of species on islands. For species like *B. samhaensis,* the *Begonia* collection at the Royal Botanic Garden Edinburgh is both a vital research tool and a crucial insurance against extinction.

Specimen notes | Grown from seed collected on Samha in 1999.

Location | Edinburgh (not on public display).

Conservation status | VU

74

Begonia karangputihensis

Our second *Begonia*, *B. karangputihensis*, is named for Bukit Karang Putih (White Coral Hill), a limestone peak in Lubuk Kilangan district of West Sumatra.

Begonia karangputihensis is known from only a few populations around the edge of an industrial limestone mine run by Semen Padang, Indonesia's state-owned cement manufacturing company. Here, the *Begonia* grows in shallow caves and shaded crevices in the limestone rock. Tropical limestone mountains often host a rich endemic flora, so any industrial activity, even on a local scale, can potentially cause species extinctions.

The species bears heart-shaped green leaves, which are reddish at the centre, and clusters of 10–20 delicate white flowers. Each plant has separate male and female flowers, with the male flowers maturing before the females. In many species, this strategy has evolved to prevent self-pollination, maintaining genetic diversity.

The first record of *B. karangputihensis* – a collection found in the herbarium of Andalas University, Padang – dates back to 1981. However, the species was not formally described and given a scientific name until 2015, by a team of scientists from the Royal Botanic Garden Edinburgh, Bogor Herbarium, and Bogor Botanic Garden.

Perilously situated at the entrance to an industrial limestone mine.

This species is not currently protected, lying just outside the Kerinci Seblat National Park. It was described so recently that its conservation status has not yet made it to the IUCN Red List, but it is considered to be at the very least vulnerable to extinction. Scientists at the Royal Botanic Garden Edinburgh continue to work with colleagues around the world, identifying and describing many species of *Begonia* new to science each year, to enable us to conserve and monitor them in this changing world.

Specimen notes | Grown from seed collected in 2011 on a joint expedition with a team from Bogor Herbarium.

Location | Edinburgh (Glasshouses).

Conservation status | VU (proposed)

Aloe springatei-neumannii

Known only from Kenya, *Aloe springatei-neumannii* (Asphodelaceae – asphodel family) is known from only two sites perhaps 100 kilometres apart in broken or shrubby forest around Kendu Bay at the north-east corner of Lake Victoria.

First collected in 1991 by Michael Neumann of Bonn Botanic Garden, the species was only described in 2011, by Leonard Newton of Kenyatta University in Nairobi. It was a second collection of this *Aloe*, made by the Royal Botanic Garden Edinburgh's Lawrie Springate, which convinced Newton it was an unnamed species. The double-barrelled epithet recognises both plant collectors. Sadly, Lawrie Springate died suddenly in June 2011, not knowing that he had been honoured in this way.

A yellow-flowered Aloe from the shores of Lake Victoria.

Aloe springatei-neumannii is a handsome plant, believed to be grown in cultivation locally, where its yellow flowers provide a perfect contrast to the widely grown red-flowered *A. lateritia* (*mlalangao*).

Little is known about the conservation status of either wild population of *A. springatei-neumannii*. Gwasi Hills, the area in which Springate made his collection, is a community conserved area, but all forest there has been destroyed for subsistence agriculture, which does not bode well for the species.

All aloes are protected by CITES, because their popularity for both cosmetics and horticulture makes them vulnerable to unsustainable levels of harvesting from the wild. Trade in *A. springatei-neumannii*

is heavily regulated through its listing on CITES Appendix II.

Specimen notes | Collected by Lawrie Springate and colleagues in Kenya in 1999. Entered the Royal Botanic Garden Edinburgh collection in 2004.

Location | Edinburgh (Glasshouses).

Conservation status | EN

Siliquamomum oreodoxa

Although the ginger genus *Siliquamomum* (Zingiberaceae) was known as long ago as 1895, for more than a century it was thought to contain only one species: *S. tonkinense*. Then, between 2010 and 2017, three new species were scientifically described.

Siliquamomum oreodoxa was the first of these, named in 2010 by Ngoc Sâm Lý of the Institute of Tropical Biology, Ho Chi Minh City, Vietnam, Sovanmoly Hul of Paris, and Jana Leong-Škorničková of Singapore Botanic Garden – a long-term collaborator with the Royal Botanic Garden Edinburgh's ginger team.

The species was named from the Greek *oreo* ('of the mountains') and *doxa* ('glory'), and when it flowers it certainly is glorious! It bears clusters of large white blooms, set off by a dark green and yellow patch at the centre of the labellum.

Specimen notes | Grown from a cutting collected by Sovanmoly Hul and Ngoc Sâm Lý in 2008.

Location | Edinburgh (Glasshouses).

Conservation status | EN

Siliquamomum oreodoxa is unique to Vietnam and found at only two sites, in the moist and shady conditions of primary forest. Although one population is protected within Bidoup Nui Ba National Park, and the second in Hon Ba Nature Reserve, agricultural activity and road construction continue in close proximity, posing a threat to this species and its primary forest habitat.

In 2014 Škorničková, working with Vietnamese and Czech co-authors, described a third *Siliquamomum, S. alcicorne*, and in 2017 a Vietnamese team named a fourth, *S. phamhoangii*. Both have very limited distributions within Vietnam, and both are considered endangered.

Siliquamomum species are like buses — nothing for ages, then three come along at once!

Aframomum kayserianum

Another member of Zingiberaceae, this ginger species is known from only a handful of herbarium specimens. Its range is restricted to a band of montane forest in the mountains of south-west Cameroon and eastern Nigeria.

German botanist Paul Preuss (1861–1926) first collected the unusual, white-flowered ginger on Mount Cameroon in 1891, and in 1892 it was named *Amomum kayserianum* by his compatriot Karl Moritz Schumann (1851–1904), for another German, a mysterious Dr Kayser.

It took 127 years to identify and correctly describe this species!

In 1904 Schumann transferred the species to the genus *Aframomum*, along with all the other species of *Amomum* from the African continent.

For the next 65 years, very little was known about *Aframomum kayserianum* apart from the single Mount Cameroon collection. In 1965, French botanist Jean Koechlin clouded the matter further by attributing a number of specimens from a different, more widespread species of *Aframomum* to *Aframomum kayserianum*.

Since then, more *Aframomum kayserianum* plants have been found in Cameroon, but thanks to the confusion caused by Koechlin's work, no-one realised their true identity. That is, until the Royal Botanic Garden Edinburgh's David Harris and Alexandra Wortley carried out a thorough revision of *Aframomum*, based on Harris' 20 years' experience of the genus in Central Africa. They finally made the connection between several different,

unidentified, white-flowered specimens from the montane forests of Cameroon and Nigeria, and Preuss' 1891 collection, uniting them all under the name *Aframomum kayserianum*.

Harris and Wortley's monograph of the genus was published in 2018, and *Aframomum kayserianum* was assessed as endangered, due to the small number of populations and risk that some of them might be impacted by agriculture or even – in the case of those on Mount Cameroon – volcanic eruptions.

Although the uses for *Aframomum kayserianum* specifically are unknown, the seeds of many *Aframomum* species are used medicinally, as an aphrodisiac, and traded as a valuable spice called *melegueta* pepper or grains of paradise. The spice was so important during colonial times that the 'Grain Coast' in present-day Liberia was named for it. *Aframomum* seeds are still used today to flavour alcoholic drinks – indeed, there is an illustration of *Aframomum* on the Bombay Sapphire gin bottle!

Specimen notes | Collected by the Royal Botanic Garden Edinburgh's David Harris in south-west Cameroon in 1999.

Location | Edinburgh (not on public display).

Conservation status | EN

Dioon spinulosum

Known in Spanish as *coyolito de cerro*, and in English as the giant dioon or gum palm (though it is not a palm, but a cycad), *Dioon spinulosum* (Zamiaceae) is found in the lowland evergreen rainforests of tropical Mexico.

With shiny, stiff, upward-pointing, bright-green leaves, the giant dioon is the tallest of all cycads, growing up to 16 metres and living up to 1,000 years. Like conifers, cycads are gymnosperms, reproducing by cones rather than flowers. The giant dioon is dioecious (having separate male and female plants), with each plant producing a single, massive cone every two to three years. The largest cone reported weighed 13 kilograms!

Although some cycad fossils have been dated back to as long as 300 million years ago – the early Permian Period – most of these represent extinct lineages, with today's cycad species thought to have evolved out of an evolutionary radiation around 12 million years ago. Today, around 65 per cent of cycads are considered threatened or endangered, and all are listed on CITES due to their huge popularity as ornamental plants.

The giant dioon is known from three disjunct sites – in Veracruz, Oaxaca and Yucatan – and it is estimated that around 70 per cent of the plants have been lost over the past two generations, due mostly to land-use change for livestock farming and ranching, and the building of dams and other water management practices. Fortunately the species is cultivated at over 100 botanic gardens around the world.

The tallest of all cycads.

Specimen notes | Two plants, both received in 1969 from the Natural History Museum in London, of undocumented provenance; both are female.

Location | Edinburgh (Glasshouses).

Conservation status | EN

Clianthus puniceus

Clianthus puniceus (Fabaceae) is one of two species of *Clianthus*, both endemic to New Zealand, whose hugely distinctive flowers have earned them an extensive range of common names – *kōwhai ngutukākā*, *kaka* beak, New Zealand parrot's bill, lobster claw and glory pea. Many of these names derive from the flowers' resemblance to the beak of the *kaka* (*Nestor meridionalis*), a large, forest-dwelling New Zealand parrot which is itself endangered, largely due to habitat loss and introduced predators.

The *kaka* beak is a justifiably popular ornamental, with an Award of Garden Merit from the Royal Horticultural Society. The scientific name *Clianthus* is from the Greek meaning 'glory flower'; *puniceus* is from the Latin for 'blood red'.

How many endangered plants can say they are named after an equally endangered bird?

The *kaka* beak is nowadays confined to a few scattered locations on New Zealand's North Island, from the far north to Hawkes Bay. It is difficult to know how many of these sites are part of the species' natural distribution, because historically it was frequently planted by the Māori people. An IUCN assessment in 1998 estimated that there were around 200 wild plants remaining; as of 2005, the New Zealand Plant Conservation Network reported that only a single wild plant had endured, near Kaipara Harbour in the north of North Island.

The *kaka* beak is threatened in the wild by summer droughts, competition from weeds, browsing goats, pigs, deer, possums and rodents, fire, erosion of unstable habitats, and illegal collecting of seedlings. Wild-origin plants from the Kaipara Harbour site are in cultivation, giving hope for the survival of this species.

Specimen notes | Our plant was already growing at Logan when it passed into the hands of the Royal Botanic Garden Edinburgh in 1969. Growing against a sunny wall, it flowers prolifically each year.

Location | Logan (entrance area).

Conservation status | EN

Tieghemella heckelii

Tieghemella heckelii (*baku*, *makore* or cherry mahogany;
Sapotaceae – miracle berry family) is an important timber species,
found in the tropical rainforests of Cameroon, Ivory Coast, Gabon,
Ghana, Liberia, Nigeria and Sierra Leone.

The trees are large and relatively fast-growing, sometimes beginning to flower and fruit after as little as 10 years. The largest may reach 55 metres tall and produce around 3,000–4,000 big, juicy fruits each year.

The fruits are a valuable food source for animals ranging from bush pigs to elephants – and here the beneficial relationship between animal and plant may well be mutual. Studies are conflicting, but many report that elephants are vital for the dispersal of *baku* seeds, allowing natural regeneration to occur, and that recent reductions in elephant numbers may negatively impact on tree populations.

At the same time, other scientists have shown that climate change is altering the fruiting patterns of many tropical African forest trees, with devastating impacts on elephant populations – and this may well be the case for *baku*.

Among humans, the seed kernels – known as *baco* – are rich in edible fat called *dumore* or *makore* butter, popular as a cooking or seasoning oil, and often preferred to palm oil.

In some parts of its range, notably Ghana and Liberia, overharvesting of *baku* for timber is a serious problem that may lead to local extinction. However, the conservation status of *baku* has not been assessed since 1998, so we cannot be certain how this species is currently faring. It is thought to be held in only two botanic gardens worldwide – few, at least in temperate regions, would be able to house such a large tree under glass.

> *Intriguing interdependence between one of Africa's largest trees and Africa's largest land animal.*

Specimen notes | Donated by the University of Aberdeen in 2011; grown in a pot to restrict its growth and enable it to be kept in the Glasshouses without breaking through the roof!

Location | Edinburgh (Glasshouses).

Conservation status |

Berberis negeriana

Berberis negeriana (Berberidaceae – barberry family), the *michay de Neger*, or Neger's barberry, is named in honour of Friedrich Wilhelm Neger (1868–1923), a German forest botanist and mycologist who spent many years in Chile exploring the country's magnificent coastal rainforest in the late 1800s, before much of it was destroyed.

Michay de Neger is one of 12 barberry species exclusive to Chile, and the second-most threatened on the mainland (the most threatened being *B. littoralis*, which grows in a coastal Atacama valley in the fog oasis zone). In the wild, *michay de Neger* is restricted to south-central Chile, where it is found in only three small areas of remnant *Nothofagus obliqua* (southern beech) forest to the south of the coastal city of Concepción. The largest subpopulation clings to life on coastal hills now cloaked almost entirely in commercial *Eucalyptus* plantations.

> *This species spent almost a century being classified as something else.*

A small evergreen shrub, barely a metre tall, it bears upright clusters of yellow flowers, followed by indigo-blue fruits hanging from the ends of the branches. Although first described in 1902, *B. negeriana* was soon subsumed into the more widespread *B. serratodentata*.

It was not until 1999 that it was recognised again as a distinctive species, and not until 2004 that it was grown in the UK, at both the Royal Botanic Garden Edinburgh and Chile-Argentina specialists Nymans Garden, West Sussex. Observation of the species in cultivation has allowed scientists to see how very distinctive it is and assess it as endangered – a status which has not yet been officially recognised by the IUCN – providing evidence to support conservation efforts of this rare and threatened plant.

Specimen notes | Grown from seed collected in 2004 by Paulina Hechenleitner Vega, who worked with the Royal Botanic Garden Edinburgh for many years and is now coordinator of Chilean conservation and outdoor learning charity Fundación Chilco.

Location | Benmore; Edinburgh (Chilean Terrace Garden).

Conservation status | EN (proposed)

Amorphophallus titanum

One of the most famous of all threatened plants, due to its immense size and unpleasant smell, *Amorphophallus titanum* (Araceae – arum family) is known as *krubi* and *bunga bangui* in its native Indonesia, and titan arum or corpse flower elsewhere. Its scientific name comes from the Greek, *Amorphophallus* meaning 'misshapen phallus' and *titanum* meaning 'giant'.

Long recognised by Indigenous people, it was brought to Europe by Italian botanist Odoardo Beccari (1843–1920) and first flowered in cultivation at the Royal Botanic Gardens, Kew, in 1889.

Titan arum boasts the world's largest unbranched inflorescence. The tallest ever recorded was 3.7 metres tall at Cibodas Botanical Garden, Indonesia, in 2016. However, the official Guinness World Record holder is a 3.1 metre giant grown in Gifford, New Hampshire, USA, in 2010.

The stench emitted by the titan arum mimics that of rotting flesh, attracting its pollinators: carrion beetles, flies, and sweat bees. The Royal Botanic Garden Edinburgh's titan arum is nicknamed 'New Reekie' – a play on the nickname for Edinburgh, Auld Reekie, and the fact that the bloom smells terrible!

Specimen notes | Grown from seed at Hortus Botanicus Leiden, Netherlands, in 2002, and gifted to the Royal Botanic Garden Edinburgh in 2003.

Location | Edinburgh (Glasshouses).

Conservation status | EN

It was gifted to the Royal Botanic Garden Edinburgh from the Netherlands as a corm the size of an orange. By 2010, it weighed a record-breaking 153.9 kilograms – about the same as a full-grown panda – and had to be weighed on scales borrowed from the elephants at Edinburgh Zoo.

New Reekie has flowered three times, in 2015, 2017 and 2019. The last was the tallest, at 2.81 metres. It has been propagated several times to produce offspring, via leaf cuttings, corm splits, and most recently by seed, being fertilised by hand using pollen shared by the Eden Project in Cornwall.

Titan arum is endangered in the wild due to destruction of its forest habitat. The Royal Botanic Garden Edinburgh is part of a global collaborative project to map the genetic diversity of cultivated titan arums worldwide using a technique called DNA fingerprinting. By identifying which plants are clones and which are most distantly related, we can focus on propagating rarer genotypes and breeding to maintain diversity and minimise the risk of extinction.

From the size of an orange to the weight of a giant panda.

Encephalartos lebomboensis

Despite their tough leaves and formidable spines, evolved as protection against browsing herbivores, cycads are some of the most vulnerable species on Earth today. *Encephalartos lebomboensis* (Zamiaceae) – *isigqiki-somkhovu* in Zulu, or the Lebombo cycad – is now found in the wild at only five sites, comprising perhaps 5,000 individuals in total.

The Lebombo cycad was first formally described in 1949 by South African botanist Inez Verdoorn (1896–1989). Its name reflects its distribution in the Lebombo Mountains of South Africa, Mozambique and Eswatini.

> *These ancient survivors are more at risk than they have ever been.*

However, the Lebombo cycad reached Scotland decades before this, as early as the 1920s when a Captain Keith, of Ravelston in Edinburgh, discovered a colony of the plants and transplanted them to his estate. Keith also sent plants to Kirstenbosch National Botanical Garden in South Africa and Ewanrigg Botanical Garden, Zimbabwe.

Despite being CITES-listed, the Lebombo cycad's general trend is still downwards, due to multiple threats including habitat loss and degradation, and illegal collecting – the cycad is a popular species in cultivation. Some populations are protected within the Mlawula Nature Reserve and Itala Game Reserve, but the future of the species also depends on *ex-situ* conservation at the 50 or so botanic gardens where it is grown around the world.

Specimen notes | Two cultivated Lebombo cycads were received at the Garden in the 1960s.

Location | Edinburgh (Glasshouses).

Conservation status | EN

Medusagyne oppositifolia

Found only on Mahé, the largest island in the Seychelles archipelago, *Medusagyne oppositifolia* (Medusagynaceae) gets its scientific name from its flowers' resemblance to the snake-haired Medusa of Greek mythology, and its common name, jellyfish tree, from the shape of its fruits.

The small tree is the only species in the genus *Medusagyne* (and, indeed the family Medusagynaceae, although it is sometimes placed within the larger family Ochnaceae).

It was once thought to be extinct, but was rediscovered in 1970 by tropical forester John Procter (1927–1979).

Growing on granite outcrops – the only place where it escapes competition from invasive species – only four populations of plants remain, three of them comprising numbers in single figures. The largest, at Bernica, has 78 trees, and is the only population producing seedlings.

The jellyfish tree with snake-like flowers.

The jellyfish tree is threatened by fire, habitat disturbance due to human activity, and competition from species introduced by humans. These are compounded by low levels of regeneration and high seed mortality, most likely due to inbreeding depression in the small populations remaining.

Fortunately, seedlings have been germinated successfully in nurseries in the Seychelles, as well as at the Royal Botanic Garden Edinburgh, where plants have now been growing since 2003.

Specimen notes | Grown from seed collected on Mahé, Seychelles, in 2003.

Location | Edinburgh (not on public display).

Conservation status | CR

Cedrus atlantica

Cedrus atlantica (Pinaceae) – the Atlantic or Atlas cedar – is a conifer growing wild only in the mountains of Morocco and Algeria in north-west Africa. The Atlas cedar can grow up to 40 metres tall and nine metres in girth, often smaller at higher elevations, with attractive green or grey-blue foliage.

First introduced to the UK around 1840, a tree planted by Lord Somers in 1845 is – at the time of publication – still growing well at Eastnor Castle in Herefordshire. At the Royal Botanic Garden Edinburgh there is a grey-blue-leaved example in front of the Herbaceous Border, but

An Atlas cedar graces the South Lawn of the US White House — and contains a tree house built for President Carter's daughter.

perhaps the most famous is the tree by the pond, which was planted in 1908. New, known provenance plants were introduced from Morocco in 2015.

An Atlas cedar growing at the US White House in Washington, DC contains a tree house designed personally by President Carter and built for his daughter, Amy. The structure is self-supporting and does not cause damage to the tree.

In the wild, the Atlas cedar faces many threats. It has been heavily and increasingly exploited for its strong, durable timber, and for essential oils, distilled from the timber and foliage. Throughout its range up to 75 per cent of trees were lost between 1940 and 1982. Since the 1980s, droughts, particularly in areas adjacent to the Sahara, have led to even further losses.

Multiple pests have exacerbated the recent decline, including processionary moth caterpillars which destroy the foliage, Barbary macaques which strip bark from the trees, and cedar bark beetles causing widespread damage.

Many stands of trees are now located within national parks, where they receive some protection, and programmes are in place to monitor the extent and severity of recent dieback.

Ex-situ conservation has become difficult due to *Sirococcus* blight, now widespread in the British Isles, but since 1991 the Royal Botanic Garden Edinburgh's International Conifer Conservation Programme has distributed more than 250 trees across a network of safe sites including our own Gardens at Benmore and Dawyck, helping to ensure the species' future.

Specimen notes | Our oldest Atlas cedar, by the pond at Edinburgh, was planted in 1908. The first of documented provenance is from Jebel Tazekha in Morocco and was supplied by Milde Botanic Garden, Norway, in 1974 – it is growing at Benmore.

Location | Benmore (Avenue); Dawyck; Edinburgh (Pond Lawn).

Conservation status |

Streptocarpus stomandrus

Streptocarpus stomandrus is a herbaceous perennial with velvety leaves and blueish-purple tubular flowers. It was first described by the Royal Botanic Garden Edinburgh's Bill Burtt in 1958, from collections made in 1943 by Winifred Moreau, wife of ornithologist Reginald Ernest Moreau (1897–1970), and after whom Winifred's warbler (*Scepomycter winifredae*) is named.

At first, *Streptocarpus stomandrus* was known only from Moreau's collection in the Nguru Mountains of Tanzania. However, the plant was rediscovered – albeit inadvertently – more than half a century later. In 2005, scientists from the Royal Botanic Garden Edinburgh, collecting in Morogoro to the south, thought they had collected the more common, closely related *Streptocarpus bambuseti*, but back in Edinburgh the plants were verified as *Streptocarpus stomandrus*.

Three of those plants are still growing in the Glasshouses. Perhaps more importantly for

conservation, some of the original seeds are stored in the seed bank, along with a supply of next-generation seeds. In the wild, the species' habitat suffers from forest fragmentation and habitat degradation, so continued propagation in botanic gardens is likely vital to its future.

The parent of many popular hybrid Cape primrose cultivars.

Streptocarpus stomandrus has been used in horticulture since the 1970s, as a hybrid parent in breeding new *Streptocarpus* (Cape primrose) cultivars, which are popular as ornamentals. Its flowers differ from most other *Streptocarpus* as the stamens (male floral parts) are attached close to the outer edge of the petals and are visible outside the upper lip of the flower; in other *Streptocarpus* the stamens are hidden inside the petals.

Specimen notes | Grown from cuttings taken in Tanzania in 2005, and seed collected in 2013.

Location | Edinburgh (not on public display).

Conservation status |

Araucaria araucana

Known in Chile as *pehuén*, *Araucaria araucana* is perhaps more widely recognised under its common name: monkey puzzle. Native to central and southern Chile, and western Argentina, this conifer is a popular ornamental. In the wild it is found in the Andes and Chile's coastal mountains, with a preferred – if risky – habitat of the slopes of volcanoes.

Legend tells that the monkey puzzle was introduced to the UK when Scottish surgeon Archibald Menzies (1754–1842) pocketed seed at a banquet in Santiago, and sent it back to the Royal Botanic Gardens, Kew.

> *Many urban myths have grown up around Chile's iconic national tree.*

It is far more likely, however, that the seed was sent to Menzies from southern Chile while he was staying in Valparaíso.

Another popular tale surrounds how the monkey puzzle got its name. The story goes that in the 1830s barrister Charles Austin (1799–1874) remarked on viewing a planting of the tree at Sir William Molesworth's Pencarrow House, Cornwall, that, "It would even puzzle a monkey to climb that tree".

Monkey puzzles can grow up to 50 metres tall and live to 2,000 years. Most are either male or female – some rare examples display both sexes. The light, soft wood is sought-after for lumber, flooring, paper pulp and ship masts, although international trade is now banned.

Monkey puzzle seeds are very rich in nutrients, and were once an essential part of Indigenous people's diet – boiled or roasted, they taste rather like chestnuts and are still sometimes eaten today. Austral parakeets (*Enicognathus ferrugineus*) also seem to enjoy them, and can be seen removing seeds from the female cones in autumn, through which they are largely responsible for the species' dispersal.

The monkey puzzle's looks made it very popular in Europe in the Victorian and Edwardian eras, and it can frequently be seen in parks and gardens, where our jays and squirrels seem to have taken to the seeds as much as the parakeets of its homeland.

The biggest threat to *A. araucana* in the wild is fire, with very large areas of forest – including national parks – affected. The International Conifer Conservation Programme is working with non-governmental organisation Rainforest Concern to protect the species in Chile and plant trees at safe sites in the British Isles.

Specimen notes | Cultivated at the Royal Botanic Garden Edinburgh for over 200 years. Our oldest living monkey puzzles have been at Benmore since 1872. Since 1991 many seed collections have been made in Chile and are planted at safe sites around the British Isles.

Location | Benmore (Chilean Hillside); Edinburgh (opposite Glasshouse range).

Conservation status |

Coffea arabica

Coffee is one of the most important of all commercial crop plants, providing a livelihood for 100 million people.

The genus *Coffea* – and the species *C. arabica* (Rubiaceae – coffee family) – was established by Swedish botanist Carl Linnaeus (1707–1778) in his 1753 *Species Plantarum*. Over 100 species of *Coffea* have been described, but only two are grown commercially – *C. arabica* and *C. canephora*, more widely known as 'robusta'.

Coffea arabica is an evergreen shrub with sweetly scented white flowers and red berries, referred to in the coffee trade as cherries. Each cherry contains two seeds, ('beans'), which are dried, roasted and ground. Each plant can produce between 0.5 and 5.5 kilograms of coffee beans per year. *Arabica* coffee makes up around 70 per cent of the world's coffee output and as much as 95 per cent in South America.

Coffea arabica is now known to be an ancient hybrid of *C. canephora* and another species, *C. eugenioides*. Although native to Sudan, South Sudan, Ethiopia and Kenya, and first domesticated in Ethiopia, *C. arabica* is so called because Linnaeus' original description was based on plants from Yemen. With the first record of coffee being drunk there dating from 1450, by the end of the sixteenth century Yemen became a major centre for the trade. At the heart of Yemen's coffee trade was the port of Mokha, from which we get the terms *mocha* and *moka*.

> *One of the world's top 10 most traded commodities.*

Today, wild coffee populations in Ethiopia and South Sudan are threatened by deforestation, development and, increasingly, climate change causing drought and extreme temperatures. The coffee berry borer (*Hypothenemus hampei*) is also an ever-more significant pest for coffee crops around the world, and projected to become an accelerating threat to East Africa's wild coffee plants as temperatures rise.

Protecting wild populations of *arabica* coffee should be of great concern to all coffee-drinkers, as these contain the majority of the species' genetic diversity, a source of potential disease-, pest- and drought-resistance genes for breeding into cultivated varieties. The Yayu Coffee Forest – a UNESCO Important Biosphere Reserve – in south-west Ethiopia protects one population of wild *C. arabica*. A number of *ex-situ* gene banks have also been established both in Ethiopia and internationally in an attempt to conserve this crop wild relative's vital genetic diversity.

Specimen notes | Collected in 1999 from a small coffee farm in the Dominican Republic.

Location | Edinburgh (Glasshouses).

Conservation status | EN

Brugmansia sanguinea

Brugmansia (Solanaceae – nightshade family) – *huanduj* or angel's trumpet – comprises seven species, all extinct in the wild. There are no known herbarium collections made from confirmed wild plants, nor have there been any confirmed wild sightings in recent times.

They are presumed native to South America, where they still exist in cultivated form. The apparent absence of fruit dispersal or spontaneous regeneration from the plants, despite the presence of large numbers of fruits containing viable seeds, suggests that their animal dispersers may have also become extinct – although this may be only part of the reason for the plants' decline.

> *Highly psychoactive, Brugmansia plays a key role in many South American Indigenous rituals.*

Among the most toxic of all ornamental plants, traditionally *Brugmansia* were used by Indigenous people for a wide range of spiritual and medicinal purposes, including as an entheogen – a psychoactive substance used in religious or spiritual rituals. One of the many alkaloids angel's trumpets contain is scopolamine (hyoscine, known colloquially as *burundanga* or devil's breath). Scopolamine is used in conventional medicine to prevent motion sickness, usually via a transdermal patch, and can also be derived from many other members of the family Solanaceae, such as the nightshades. Of course, Solanaceae also contains many generally harmless and delicious species such as tomatoes, potatoes, peppers, chillies and aubergines.

The multiple uses of *Brugmansia* within Indigenous cultures – for which they were widely planted – are probably what have allowed them to survive thus far. However, all seven species are now considered threatened with total extinction of even naturalised and cultivated plants across their range. They are regularly eradicated from gardens for fear of their toxicity and supposedly 'evil' nature, and in response to illegal use of the drugs produced from them.

At the same time, the cultural traditions and knowledge of Indigenous people are progressively being lost. Maintaining and rehabilitating Indigenous customs, alongside education about the cultural and practical value of these species, may be needed to help save the angel's trumpets from extinction.

The Royal Botanic Garden Edinburgh cultivates living plants of *B. sanguinea*, for which common names include *guamuco* and red angel's trumpet.

Specimen notes | Supplied as cuttings from the Royal Botanic Gardens, Kew, in 1979, and one plant already growing at Logan when the Garden was acquired in 1969.

Location | Edinburgh (not on display); Logan.

Conservation status | EW

Fitzroya cupressoides

The Patagonian cypress, known as *lawal* in Mapuche and *alerce* in Spanish, is the only species in the genus *Fitzroya* (Cupressaceae), and is native to Chile and Argentina. This conifer can attain massive proportions, up to 60 metres tall with a girth over 10 metres – though Charles Darwin reported seeing examples almost 40 metres in girth! It is also exceptionally long-lived: the oldest is estimated at 3,620 years old, making it the second-oldest tree on Earth after the Great Basin bristlecone pine (*Pinus longaeva*) of the south-west USA.

The genus name *Fitzroya* honours Vice Admiral Robert Fitzroy (1805–1865), captain of HMS *Beagle*, on which Charles Darwin made his famous 1831–1836 voyage of discovery including the Pacific coast of Chile and Ecuador's Galápagos Islands.

Patagonian cypress wood is highly valued for its resistance to heat and humidity, making it excellent for carpentry, musical instruments and shingles. Fibres from the inner bark have been used for ship caulking, and the resin is burned as incense. The wood was considered so precious that, in southern Chile in the nineteenth century, *Fitzroya* shingles and boards were used as currency. Evidence of the trees' extraordinary rot-resistance is provided by ancient wood, buried in bogs, which has been recovered and used.

The species was first introduced to the UK by William Lobb (1809–1864), of Veitch and Sons' Nurseries, in 1849. Today, the International Conifer Conservation Programme's network of safe sites supports over 500 of these

Named for the captain of HMS Beagle, which carried Charles Darwin on his famous voyage around the world.

trees. One has been planted in the grounds of Ampton Hall, Suffolk, birthplace of Admiral Fitzroy, and another at Down House in Bromley, Charles Darwin's family home.

The Patagonian cypress' decline can largely be linked to historic logging and fires. The clearance associated with European colonisation comprises one of the most massive and rapid deforestation events in South America. One famous, intentional, fire took advantage of a drought in 1863 to destroy the forest from Puerto Varas to Puerto Montt in Chile – a distance of 20 kilometres.

Fitzroya cupressoides is now protected under CITES, and in Chile the tree has been declared a National Monument.

Specimen notes | Our oldest living *Fitzroya* is at Benmore, and dates from 1927. Since 1988 the International Conifer Conservation Programme has made many wild collections, mostly cuttings, in Chile, and these can be seen in all four Gardens.

Location | Benmore (Chilean Hillside); Dawyck; Edinburgh; Logan.

Conservation status | EN

Sabal bermudana

Sabal bermudana (Arecaceae – palm family) is the only palm endemic to Bermuda, where it grows in forested wetlands. It is commonly called the sabal palm, Bermuda palmetto, Bermuda cabbage palm or bibby tree. Ripe fruits from the bibby tree provide food for birds and other animals, as well as liquor for human consumption: historically, holes were drilled into the tree's trunk, and the sap extracted to make *bibby* – a strong alcoholic drink. The practice was outlawed by the Governor of Bermuda in 1627.

The sabal palm at the Royal Botanic Garden Edinburgh was, until 2021, one of the oldest plants in the entire Living Collection and probably the oldest palm in Scotland. It is believed to have been shipped nearly 4,000 miles from Bermuda to Germany and on to Edinburgh's Port of Leith in the 1790s, when it was planted at the Royal Botanic Garden's then site, off Leith Walk.

Edinburgh's famous travelling tree.

In 1820, Garden staff, led by Curator William McNab (1780–1848), began a three-year process of moving all the plants to the present site at Inverleith. In order to salvage the many large, mature specimens growing at Leith Walk, McNab devised an amazing 'transplanting machine', drawn by a dozen horses, to carry them across the city. In this way, the sabal palm was moved in 1822, first to a lean-to Glasshouse. In 1858 – weighing an estimated 7–8 tonnes – it was transported to the spectacular new Victorian Temperate Palm House, and in 1874 it made its final journey, to the octagonal Tropical Palm House, where it remained for almost 150 years.

In 2021, at well over 200 years old and reaching the end of its life, this emblematic tree – which had already had to be trimmed several times to prevent it breaking through the roof of the Glasshouse – was dismantled from the top down.

Knowing that the sabal palm couldn't last forever, in 2016 the Indoor Team lovingly propagated several young plants from the fated tree. These will be planted in prime positions in the new 'Edinburgh Biomes' development as a symbol of renewal, linking the Garden's past with the many generations who will pass through these Glasshouses in the future.

In the wild, populations of the sabal palm are fragmented and declining, facing habitat loss through development, and competition from multiple invasive introduced species. Continued cultivation at botanic gardens such as Edinburgh may provide the species' best hope for the future.

Specimen notes | Progeny of the Royal Botanic Garden Edinburgh's original sabal palm.

Location | Edinburgh (Glasshouses).

Conservation status | EN

Cleistocactus winteri

The distribution of *Cleistocactus winteri* (Cactaceae – cactus family) is highly localised to steep cliffs in the seasonally dry forests of the Bolivian Andes. Being only seasonally dry, the habitat can receive over 80 millimetres of rain each month for around half the year, and *C. winteri* is remarkably well adapted to deal with the wet weather. The cactus is covered in long, downward-pointed spines which allow rainfall and run-off to drain rapidly. The flower is equally adapted to its ecological niche: bird-pollinated, it is cleverly shaped to prevent thieving insects from accessing its nectar.

Cleistocactus winteri was first formally described by German botanist Friedrich Ritter (1898–1989) in 1962. It is now split into two subspecies: the golden rat tail cactus (subspecies *winteri*), to which the Royal Botanic Garden Edinburgh plant belongs,

and the white-spined monkey's tail cactus (subspecies *colademono*), discovered as recently as 2000, and now grown as a spectacular pot plant all over the world. The whole *C. winteri* species is endangered.

A cactus that doesn't mind the rain!

The Royal Botanic Garden Edinburgh has a research focus on seasonally dry forests – the underappreciated, highly biodiverse cousins of tropical rainforest. In 2020, with a network of local partners, we published a methodological approach to monitoring the health of these 'forgotten forests', aiming to keep track of their biodiversity and to target conservation interventions in the face of climate change and other threats.

The limited distribution of *C. winteri* puts it at risk from natural disasters such as landslides, or development such as road construction. However, the main threat to both subspecies remains collection for the cactus trade. Their popularity as ornamentals and slow-growing nature mean it remains highly profitable to collect plants from the wild. For this reason, all wild cacti are listed on CITES.

Specimen notes | Propagated from the original collection made in Bolivia by Ritter.

Location | Edinburgh (Glasshouses).

Conservation status | EN

Fraxinus americana

The white ash, *Fraxinus americana* (Oleaceae – olive family), is native to the eastern and central USA, has been introduced to Hawaii, and may also be present in northern Mexico. Historically the most common, widespread and useful of North America's ash trees, its wood has been made into bows, baseball bats, tool handles, guitars, veneers and joinery. The seeds also provide food for birds and squirrels.

America's white ash population has been devastated by the emerald ash borer (*Agrilus planipennis*), a flat-headed beetle introduced accidentally from Asia to Detroit in the 1990s, though its presence was undiscovered until 2002. The borer has spread rapidly across much of the tree's natural range and feeds on all ash species it has encountered.

Eighty per cent of these once widespread trees are expected to be lost over the coming century.

The larvae feed in the phloem (the plant's nutrient transport vessels), effectively girdling the tree, causing virtually 100 per cent mortality within six years once present in a population. The borer persists in forests, even when low numbers of ash trees remain, possibly by switching to alternative hosts until the ash becomes available. Thus it is able to infest any emerging ash saplings rapidly, preventing regeneration. Unless an effective control is developed, 80 per cent of white ash trees are predicted to succumb over the next century.

Despite considerable investment into chemical and biological control, and genetic research to identify any natural resistance, no effective control has yet been found for North America's emerald ash borer infestation. The best hope for the white ash's survival at present is via botanic gardens and seed banks outside the continent.

The emerald ash borer has not yet been recorded in the UK, and it is vital to remain vigilant for its accidental introduction. The Royal Botanic Garden Edinburgh is part of the International Plant Sentinel Network, a global programme linking botanic gardens and plant protection organisations working to provide an early warning system for new and emerging plant pests and pathogens.

Should the borer arrive in the UK, it would considerably hamper efforts to protect our European ash – *F. excelsior* – already struggling due to the fungal disease ash dieback (*Hymenoscyphus fraxineus*). Efforts are ongoing to breed *F. excelsior* lines resistant to ash dieback, but ideally these would also need to be unpalatable to the emerald ash borer!

Specimen notes | Our oldest collection, at Edinburgh, was made in Oregon. Additional trees at Dawyck, Edinburgh and Benmore originate from wild populations in Ohio, Massachusetts and Pennsylvania.

Location | Benmore; Dawyck; Edinburgh.

Conservation status |

Azorina vidalii

54

The Azores bellflower, *Azorina vidalii* (Campanulaceae – bellflower family), is found only in Portugal's Azores archipelago. A small evergreen shrub, it bears white or pink bell-shaped flowers, with glands at their base producing sweet nectar to attract pollinating insects.

Specimen notes | Our Edinburgh plant was grown from seed originally collected in the Azores and supplied in 2016 via Basel University Botanical Garden and Berlin-Dahlem Botanical Garden. Logan's is a cultivated specimen of unknown origin.

Location | Edinburgh (Glasshouses); Logan (not on public display).

Conservation status | EN

The bellflower is almost as old as the islands themselves: genetic studies by a European team in 2012 have shown that it diverged from its closest sister lineage approximately 8.3 million years ago, which is roughly the time Santa Maria – the first island the bellflower colonised – was formed by seismic and volcanic activity under the seas of the Atlantic Ocean.

> *A species as old as the islands it inhabits.*

The bellflower has a fragmented population, comprising fewer than 1,000 mature plants, growing in a variety of habitats from rocky shores and cliffs to pebble or sandy beaches and platforms of compacted lava.

The leaves of the Azores bellflower are edible, and sweet when eaten raw. They can be used in place of lettuce in salads, though the plants are not very productive. When harvesting, it is important to take only individual side leaves – if the growing tip is harvested, the shoot will usually die.

The main threat to the species is habitat loss through a combination of avalanches and landslides, introduced invasive species, and commercial development. The bellflower is listed as a priority species on Annex II of the European Habitats Directive and under Appendix I of the Bern Convention, both recognising the urgency of the situation facing the Azores bellflower.

Juglans cinerea

Known as the butternut (though nothing to do with butternut squash), white walnut or *noyer cendré*, *Juglans cinerea* (Juglandaceae – walnut family) is a riverside tree found across most of the eastern USA and Canada.

Like many walnuts, the butternut is valued for its timber, which is used for cabinets, furniture and carving. Its nuts are edible and may be pickled or ground into flour, the sap is sometimes tapped as a drink, and the bark, roots and husks are traditionally used in medicine – often as a laxative – or as a yellow dye. Butternut dye was associated with homespun clothing, and 'butternut' was a derogatory nickname given, in the mid-nineteenth century, to people from the southern States where it was commonly used. Later it was also applied to Confederate soldiers whose uniforms tended to fade to the same colour.

> *When is a butternut not a butternut? When it's a buartnut (or a butterbuart)!*

Although the butternut grows across a wide range, it is not abundant anywhere. A rapid decline in numbers over the past half-century is attributed to the deadly fungal pest *Ophiognomonia clavigignenti-juglandacearum* (butternut canker), first reported in the Americas in 1967. The canker is now found right across the species' range, spread either by water or by insects, and has caused the loss of up to 80 per cent of butternut trees, compounded by habitat degradation, poor regeneration and genetic dilution.

Efforts are being made to find ways to control butternut canker. Some mature, apparently uninfected trees still stand and may harbour genes for resistance. Harvesting from these remaining individuals is now controlled, to give their genotypes a chance to persist.

Hybrids of butternut and Japanese walnut (*J. ailantifolia*) – known as 'buartnuts' – are resistant to butternut canker. Backcrossing buartnuts with butternuts produces the unlikely named butterbuarts: still resistant, but with more butternut characteristics. Most of the ornamental trees that look like butternuts in North America are now actually buartnuts or butterbuarts. The Royal Botanic Garden Edinburgh's trees are pure butternuts.

Specimen notes | Two trees collected as seed in Ontario and supplied via the University of Guelph Arboretum.

Location | Edinburgh (Copse and Oak Lawn).

Conservation status | EN

Legrandia concinna

52

This small evergreen tree is the only species of *Legrandia* (Myrtaceae – myrtle family). It is unique to Chile where it is also called *luma del norte*, or *luma blanca*.

Growing to around eight metres tall, it bears large, extremely glossy, dark-green leaves which are a deep plum-red when they emerge, showy cream flowers, large spherical red fruits, and attractive flaky bark similar to that of a *Eucalyptus* (which is also in the myrtle family).

The leaves of *luma del norte* display an unusual ecological feature dubbed

'domatia': small cavities on their underside, in the axis of the main veins, which are inhabited by ants or mites. Domatia have evolved independently in several different lineages of tropical trees to promote a mutually beneficial relationship: the plant provides a home for the insect and some protection from predators, while the insect feeds on pests which could be harmful to the plant.

Provides a home for ants, which in turn protect it from pests: win-win!

Legrandia concinna is known from only a few small populations in south-central Chile, where it is threatened by habitat loss due to deforestation, and fire. This region's forests are disappearing at an alarming rate – some 64 per cent in the last 30 years – largely through the conversion of natural forest to commercial plantations of Monterey pine (*Pinus radiata*) and *Eucalyptus*.

The species was first introduced into cultivation in Britain and Ireland through the Royal Botanic Garden Edinburgh in 1999. With careful consideration of international conventions and benefit-sharing with the people and country of its origin, *luma del norte* has strong potential as an ornamental, which may help to conserve it for future generations.

Specimen notes | Grown from seed collected in Chile in 1999 and 2001. Several seedlings are also being nurtured in the Glasshouses at Logan (off display).

Location | Edinburgh (Glasshouses); Logan (outside).

Conservation status | EN

Sequoiadendron giganteum

Sequoiadendron giganteum (Cupressaceae), the giant sequoia or giant redwood, is among the most famous of all endangered plant species, and is one of three conifer species widely known as redwoods. It certainly is a giant, growing up to 95 metres tall and 47 metres in girth. Individuals may live over 3,000 years, thanks to their rot-resistant wood, thick, fireproof bark, and stability in high winds.

Previously exploited commercially, despite the timber being fibrous and brittle, most wild populations are now in protected areas where the redwood groves are a popular tourist attraction.

> *California's 'General Sherman', measured by trunk volume, is the largest single-stemmed standing tree in the world.*

Nevertheless, the giant redwood remains threatened, with its natural range reduced to the western slopes of California's Sierra Nevada. Adapted to a regime of periodic fires, contemporary fire prevention measures can increase competition from other conifer species in the mixed woodlands and reduce recruitment of new redwood trees in the dense forest. When fires do occur, they are now often more devastating: surrounding trees of more flammable species act as conduits for the flames, allowing them to reach the redwoods' vulnerable crowns.

The largest living wild redwood in California, nicknamed 'General Sherman', is 84 metres tall, 31 metres in girth, and around 2,500 years old. In cultivation, *Sequoiadendron giganteum* specimens have not yet even approached this size.

The tallest tree outside California, which at only 158 years old is a mere teenager, is found at Benmore Botanic Garden, and is 56 metres tall.

Benmore's Champion redwood is one of 49 trees forming a spectacular Redwood Avenue 350 metres long, planted in 1863, soon after the species was introduced to Europe. The Redwood Avenue is now threatened by climate change, which on Scotland's west coast is causing more frequent and intense rainfall. This is compounded by soil compaction, contributing to waterlogging and creating an ideal habitat for pathogens. At time of writing, remedial soil-drainage works are underway in the hope of saving the trees.

Specimen notes | Benmore's Redwood Avenue of 50 trees (49 surviving) was planted in 1863 by the Garden's then owner, James Piers Patrick. Edinburgh's oldest giant redwoods date from 1969. The first documented-origin plants arrived at Benmore as seed from the USA in 1974.

Location | Benmore (Redwood Avenue); Dawyck; Edinburgh (John Muir Grove).

Conservation status | EN

Rhododendron kanehirae

Rhododendron kanehirae was first described by the prolific British plant collector Ernest Henry 'Chinese' Wilson (1876–1930) in 1921, from a collection he made in 1918 in the garden of a police station in Urai (now called Wulai District), Taiwan. With delicate purple blooms, it had been widely cultivated on the island for several centuries.

In 1984, the only known wild population of the species was submerged by the new Feitsui (Emerald Lake) Reservoir caused by the damming of the Beishi River. Immediately prior to this destruction, wild plants were successfully translocated to Fushan Botanical Garden, Wulai, in an attempt to save the species from total extinction.

Four years later, in 1988, *Rhododendron kanehirae* was declared a Precious Rare Species by the government of Taiwan.

Specimen notes | Grown from seed raised at Fushan Botanical Garden from plants translocated prior to the loss of the wild population.

Location | Edinburgh (Glasshouses); Logan (outside).

Conservation status | EW

The Taiwan Endangered Species Research Institute distributed material to botanic gardens in Taiwan, Japan, the UK and the United States, with the aim of creating enough *ex-situ* conservation collections to safeguard the species.

A 10-year restoration effort saw translocated individuals of *R. kanehirae* reinstated within the Feitsui Reservoir and Dam site, close to the species' original location. Restricted access to the site (to protect the water quality of the reservoir) fortunately also protects the translocated *Rhododendrons*. In the light of this protection and the successful reintroduction, *R. kanehirae* was removed from Taiwan's list of protected plants in 2002.

The Royal Botanic Garden Edinburgh received herbarium specimens made in the wild population by Sheng-You Lu of the Taiwan Forestry Research Institute in 1983, knowing that it was likely to be destroyed. We also grow living plants under glass at Edinburgh and outside at Logan, obtained during a joint Edinburgh-Taiwan Expedition in 1993, when we were given seeds from the wild plants translocated to Fushan Botanical Garden from the banks of the Beishi River.

> *Extinct in the wild, but swift action saved the species from total annihilation.*

Meconopsis superba

The gorgeous *Meconopsis superba* (Papaveraceae – poppy family) is known from only a few locations in the Haa Valley of western Bhutan, covering a total area of only 38 square kilometres.

Along with several other *Meconopsis* (Himalayan poppies), it is a monocarpic evergreen: like our *Agave cupreata,* these plants grow for several years before producing an inflorescence, setting seed, and then dying. In the case of *M. superba,* the inflorescence bears up to 30 magnificent, pure white flowers.

> *This rare and beautiful Himalayan poppy flowers only once in its lifetime.*

Meconopsis superba was described in 1896 by David Prain (1857–1944), Scottish botanist and later Director of the Royal Botanic Gardens, Kew, from a fragment of material collected by the Lepcha collector Dungboo in 1884. Dungboo and other Lepcha people worked as professional collectors for the Calcutta Botanic Garden and the Lloyd Botanical Garden, Darjeeling. The fragment he collected can be seen in the Herbarium of the Royal Botanic Garden Edinburgh today.

The species was introduced into European cultivation in the 1920s, likely by British explorer and trophy hunter Frederick Marshman Bailey (1882–1967) and his wife Irma (1896–1988), who were in Bhutan in 1922 and passed through the Haa Valley to present the King of Bhutan with the honour of Knight Grand Commander of the Indian Empire. It first flowered in cultivation in 1927. Further living and herbarium collections were brought to the UK in the 1930s and 1940s by Himalayan plant hunters Frank Ludlow (1885–1972) and George Sherriff (1898–1967).

Although it is very common where it occurs – over 4,000 mature plants are found at one locality, Haa La – there is a continuing decline in the quality of its habitat and the number of mature individuals due to the periodic use of fire to create grazing areas. A large part of the population lies within a protected area. Climate change is a long-term threat to this species – as it is for many *Meconopsis* and other mountain species – adding to the case for its endangered classification.

Specimen notes | Of cultivated origin, supplied in 2008 by *Meconopsis* expert Ron McBeath.

Location | Edinburgh (Woodland Garden).

Conservation status | EN

Castanea dentata

The American chestnut, *Castanea dentata* (Fagaceae – beech family), is a majestic tree which formerly dominated the forests of the eastern USA, extending north to Ontario in Canada, and was of great significance to rural livelihoods as well as an important food source for native animals.

The nuts were eaten raw or cooked, ground into flour, used as a source of oil and even as a coffee or chocolate substitute. The bark is a rich source of tannins and the timber is durable, if not very strong, used widely for furniture and fence posts.

Tragically, chestnut blight (*Cryphonectria parasitica*), an airborne fungus introduced in the late 1800s, reduced the American chestnut population to an estimated 0.01 per cent of its original size by 1950, and remains a threat today. Chestnut blight does not affect the roots, but kills the canopy, thus rendering the species functionally extinct in the wild but allowing diseased stumps to continue to send up sprouts, spreading the disease.

The blight was first identified at Bronx Zoo in 1904, and was originally thought to have been imported on Chinese chestnuts (*Castanea mollissima*) introduced from China.

Specimen notes | Two trees at Edinburgh, added to the Collection in 1940 and 1968. The former, supplied by Hillier and Sons' nursery, is a UK Champion Tree.

Location | Edinburgh (Azalea Lawn and *Berberis* Beds).

Conservation status | CR

More recent, genetic work suggests that the blight came to America twice, from Japan and one other, unknown source.

In the USA, attempts are being made to create a more resistant population by crossing *Castanea dentata* with *Castanea mollissima*, which has high levels of immunity due to its natural coevolution with the pathogen.

A chestnut that can be used in place of coffee, and even chocolate!

In Europe, the blight is controlled to some degree through biocontrol, using a virus that decreases the fungus' ability to cause disease, but there is too much genetic diversity within American populations of the fungus for this to be effective. Chestnut blight has been recorded at several locations in the UK between 2011 and 2018, but so far none has been found in Scotland.

The Royal Botanic Garden Edinburgh – a leading partner in Scotland's Centre for Expertise in Plant Health – is on the lookout for the disease as part of the International Plant Sentinel Network. The general public can help by reporting suspected sightings of chestnut blight (or any other emerging plant pathogen) via Forest Research's TreeAlert website.

Pitavia punctata

The remarkable specialised flora of south-central Chile includes the evergreen *Pitavia punctata* (Rutaceae – citrus family), known locally as *pitao*. Much of the plant life of this region is highly threatened and could soon disappear if present trends continue.

This tree has leaves pitted with small, semi-transparent glands (hence the epithet, *punctata*) containing essential oils, a defence against harmful predators. The citrus family is rich in essential oils such as bergamot and orange oil. In a good flowering season, *pitao* is covered in small, pure white flowers, followed in autumn by small clusters of egg-shaped fruits.

Research suggests this tree could be useful in treating cardiovascular disease.

Field research suggests that the wild distribution of *pitao* comprises fewer than 1,000 mature trees in relatively small, fragmented populations, mostly along small water courses. Over the past 30 years, *pitao* has been severely threatened by fire and deforestation. Most populations are surrounded by 'green deserts' – commercial plantations of Monterey pine (*Pinus radiata*) and *Eucalyptus* – and encroachment by these introduced species is an ongoing threat.

One beneficial adaptation of several tree species in this fire-prone region – including *pitao* – is their unusual ability to resprout new growth from the base of the plant, even if the main growing shoot is destroyed by cutting or fire. Without this adaptation, *pitao* could be in an even more precarious situation than it is today.

Chile has an impressive network of protected areas, but few have been established in the coastal mountains to the south-central part of the country, one of the richest areas in endemic species. *Pitao* is protected in only three reserves, each with fewer than 100 trees.

A collaborative project in the early 2000s on Chile's threatened forest species, by the Royal Botanic Garden Edinburgh and Chilean partners Universidad Austral de Chile, brought new *pitao* plants into cultivation in the UK and elsewhere, helping ensure its survival. With research showing that these trees have antioxidant properties potentially useful in treating cardiovascular diseases, the importance of studying and conserving them is clear.

Specimen notes | First introduced into cultivation via cuttings brought to the Royal Botanic Garden Edinburgh in 1996. Further plants grown from seed collected in 2001.

Location | Edinburgh (Chilean Terrace); Logan.

Conservation status | EN

Polystichum drepanum

The Madeira shield fern, *Polystichum drepanum* (Dryopteridaceae – wood ferns), is unique to the island of Madeira. It can be found on shady rocks and ledges in steep, humid, forested gorges to the north-west of the island. This is where Madeira's *laurisilva* forests persist – relicts of a previously widespread primary laurel forest now limited to small pockets on Madeira, the Azores and Canary Islands. *Laurisilva* is home to an irreplaceable suite of plants and animals, including many species – such as the Madeiran long-toed pigeon (*Columba trocaz*) – seen nowhere else in the world.

An impressive plant, *P. drepanum* has glossy green, finely divided leaves which can be almost a metre and a half in length. The remaining population of these plants is tiny – only 50 mature individuals, distributed across five sites – fortunately all within a national park.

Despite being listed as a priority species on Annex II of the European Habitats Directive and Appendix I of the Convention on the Conservation of European Wildlife and Natural Habitats, the Madeira shield fern remains at risk from habitat degradation by the spread of introduced species, landslips and fires, and disturbance and damage by tourists. Further conservation measures, including active habitat management, reintroduction programmes, research into population dynamics, and spore-banking, are needed to secure its future.

At the Royal Botanic Garden Edinburgh, spores collected on Madeira have germinated well, but this is only half the battle. Cultivating the plant from germination to maturity is challenging, particularly in Scotland, as it requires both high humidity and protection from frost.

> *An impressive fern, but tricky to cultivate.*

Specimen notes | Grown from spores of known wild origin.

Location | Edinburgh (not on public display).

Conservation status | CR

Abeliophyllum distichum

Abeliophyllum distichum, 미선나무 (*miseonnamu*) or white forsythia (Oleaceae), is the only species of *Abeliophyllum* so far described. It was formally named by Japanese botanist Takenoshin Nakai (1882–1952) in 1919. The shrub is found only in South Korea, with unconfirmed reports from southern North Korea, and forms low-growing thickets in the undergrowth of *Pinus* (pine) and *Quercus* (oak) forests.

White forsythia – a close relative of the true *Forsythia* – is widely cultivated as an ornamental for its fragrant early spring flowers. It is also used medicinally, in a similar way to witch hazel, to treat skin irritations.

> *Scented blooms are an early sign of spring.*

The species' population has been severely fragmented by deforestation and dam construction, and is now reduced to six known localities. It is further threatened by illegal harvesting for both horticultural and medicinal purposes. Most of the populations that remain are subject to intensive site management, and some new populations have been created through the translocation of plants from reservoir sites prior to their being inundated.

Studies have suggested that the white forsythia is self-incompatible (plants cannot fertilise themselves), through a mechanism called heterostyly. Most famously seen in the common primrose (*Primula vulgaris*), heterostylous plants come in two types: pin-flowered (with the female parts at the mouth of the floral tube and male parts lower down) and thrum-flowered (the opposite). Pollination is proven to be much more successful between pin and thrum flowers than pin-pin or thrum-thrum, even when artificially pollinated.

With many *A. distichum* wild populations containing few genotypes, self-incompatibility makes it unlikely the species will naturally set sufficient fertile seed to regenerate its numbers. This is confirmed by the fact that few seedlings have been seen in the wild. The species is protected in more than 100 botanic gardens around the world, but further targeted research and conservation will be needed to conserve the *in-situ* populations.

Specimen notes | Cultivated material received in 1953 from Bodnant Gardens, Cornwall.

Location | Edinburgh (Azalea Lawn).

Conservation status | EN

Cotoneaster cambricus

The UK's only *Cotoneaster, C. cambricus* (Rosaceae) is found exclusively on Wales' Great Orme peninsula, a limestone headland near Llandudno, Caernarvonshire. In Welsh it is called *creigafal y Gogarth* (rock apple of Gogarth, Gogarth being the Welsh name for Great Orme); in English it is the Great Orme berry.

A small shrub with pale pink flowers and glossy red berries, there are only six mature individuals left in the wild, confined to isolated and exposed cliffs where they get some protection from competition and grazing animals.

Controversy surrounds the identity of the Great Orme berry, with some botanists considering it to be synonymous with the European *Cotoneaster, C. integerrimus.* However, it was first recorded as long ago as 1783, and at that time was considered to be quite widespread within its locality. Its genetic profile also differs from *C. integerrimus.* As a separate species, perhaps a relict from a much larger population present before the last ice age, *C. cambricus* certainly qualifies as critically endangered.

The Great Orme berry was considerably impacted by Victorian plant collectors. More recently, grazing has been an issue – largely by Great Orme's feral population of Kashmir goats, introduced to Llandudno's Gloddaeth Hall in the nineteenth century by Major General Sir Savage Mostyn (1835–1914) from a larger herd kept for their cashmere wool at Windsor. They hit the headlines during 2020's Covid-19 lockdown for running amok in Llandudno town centre!

Probably the only UK species to be threatened by grazing Kashmiri goats!

Cotoneaster cambricus is a UK Biodiversity Action Plan species, protected under the Wildlife and Countryside Act 1981 (Schedule 8), and the Great Orme site is protected as a Site of Special Scientific Interest. Natural regeneration is limited and the species risks becoming genetically diluted by hybridisation with introduced cotoneasters from elsewhere.

Ex-situ collections of the species are held at seven botanic gardens, and a conservation programme is ongoing at the National Botanic Garden of Wales. As well as this, conservationists have supplemented the wild population with seed and plants from cultivation, with some success, bringing the total (wild and reintroduced) population up to 17 individuals.

Specimen notes | Received from Aberconwy Nursery in 1988, from which we also grew a cutting in 2012.

Location | Edinburgh (Heathland and Demonstration Gardens).

Conservation status | CR

Magnolia stellata

Hugely popular in gardens, there are over 200 species of *Magnolia* (Magnoliaceae), and many more varieties and cultivars. *Magnolia stellata*, the star magnolia, known in Japanese as シデコブシ (*shidekobushi*), is one of the most widely grown species, with delicate star-like white-pink flowers appearing on bare branches in late spring.

In the wild, the star magnolia is restricted to around 100 sites in a small area around Nagoya in central Honshu, Japan. It is estimated that there has been a 50–70 per cent decrease in the number of mature trees over the last three generations. The main threat to the species in the wild is habitat loss due to development, including construction of housing and even golf courses. At the same time, the remaining natural forests in which it grows are changing in species composition as cutting for fuelwood is reduced.

One of our most popular ornamental trees, yet endangered in the wild.

Only a few wild saplings and seedlings have been observed, suggesting something is constraining the species' reproduction: pollination studies also indicate that insect pollination is becoming less efficient. Further work has demonstrated that drier conditions are also limiting seed germination. Genetic research has shown not only inbreeding depression within the small, local populations, but also limited gene flow *between* isolated populations, which has led to their genomes diverging. Future conservation efforts will need to manage this complicated picture, enabling increased gene flow between plants from separate populations, while maintaining genetic diversity in the species as a whole.

Magnolia stellata was introduced to the UK in 1877 by Charles Maries (1851–1902), one of many British plant hunters sent to China and Japan by James Veitch and Sons' nursery in London. The huge popularity of the species among gardeners worldwide certainly mitigates the risk of extinction.

Specimen notes | Most of the Royal Botanic Garden Edinburgh's many star magnolia trees were grown from seed collected in Honshu. Our oldest dates to 1938.

Location | Benmore; Edinburgh; Logan.

Conservation status | EN

Cycas circinalis

Known in Hindi as *jangli-madan-mast-ka-phul*, *Cycas circinalis* (Cycadaceae) is also called the queen sago. It is known in the wild only from the Western Ghats of southern India. A stout-trunked cycad, it is widely cultivated in Hawaii and elsewhere in the tropics, both as a landscape plant and for cut foliage. Like *Coffea*, it was first formally named by Carl Linnaeus in *Species Plantarum*.

The queen sago grows as separate male and female trees, so at least one of each is needed for successful seed production. The males, though, try their best, churning out as much as 200 cubic centimetres of pollen each year. The reproductive cones generate heat and are said to produce a minty scent to attract insect pollinators.

Specimen notes | Origin uncertain.

Location | Edinburgh (Glasshouses).

Conservation status |

Threats to the species include land clearance, which is thought to have destroyed more than 50 per cent of the species' original habitat. Leaf harvesting for the urban floricultural market may also have had an impact. Larger examples are often felled to extract the pith, which is thought to have medicinal uses, and the seeds are harvested for food. Although the seeds of the queen sago are poisonous, they comprise a regular part of the local diet: after soaking mashed seed five times in fresh water, they are ground to make flour. Thus, despite the species being listed on CITES, the population remains in decline.

Insects love the fresh, minty smell of its cones.

The queen sago at the Royal Botanic Garden Edinburgh is very large (and, by extrapolation, very old), with a trunk around four metres long. It may possibly have been transported to its current site from the Leith Walk Garden in the 1820s – we know one such plant was moved, but the details have been lost in the mists of time. At the Inverleith site, it was housed first in the Palm House and in 1968 moved to the (then) new Orchid and Cycad House.

Beaucarnea recurvata

Growing wild in the Sierra Madre of Veracruz, central-southern Mexico, *Beaucarnea recurvata* is known as the elephant's foot palm (for the swollen, water-storing 'caudex' base of the stem) or ponytail palm (for its cascading leaves). It is not a true palm, but a member of Asparagaceae, the asparagus family.

The ponytail palm is a spectacular structural plant and produces a show of creamy yellow flowers for several weeks in the spring or summer. It is the most valued species of *Beaucarnea* on both national and international ornamental plant markets. Cultivated supplies cannot meet demand, and illegal harvesting continues despite the species' listing on CITES Appendix II to regulate this trade.

Elephant's foot or pony's tail — you decide!

Habitat loss is also a problem for the ponytail palm. The wild populations are small and the area they cover – in fragments of lowland tropical forest – is decreasing quickly. Plant extraction has also skewed the proportion of male and female plants in wild populations, reducing fertilisation and seed production rates. Even where seed is set, decreasing water availability limits germination rates, and grazing reduces the survival of seedlings.

In cultivation, the ponytail palm can be rather resilient. In 1998, when the glass in its Glasshouse at the Royal Botanic Garden Edinburgh was removed for refurbishment, the plant survived well without any protection.

Specimen notes | The exact history of our palm is unknown, but it was likely planted in 1967 when the (then) new 'Front Range' Glasshouses were opened.

Location | Edinburgh (Glasshouses).

Conservation status | CR

Rhododendron taxifolium

Known only from Mount Pulag, the highest peak on Luzon – the largest and most populous island in the Philippines – *Rhododendron taxifolium* is a tropical, epiphytic species, growing on the surface of other plants and deriving nutrients from the surrounding air and rainwater. It is found on mossy trees in montane cloud forest, within a remarkably narrow altitudinal zone, between 2,600 and 2,700 metres above sea level.

The epithet *taxifolium* means 'yew-leaved': very unusually for a *Rhododendron*, the leaves of *R. taxifolium* are small, shiny and narrow. Its delicate, pure white, bell-shaped flowers are borne in clusters of four.

Mount Pulag, a dormant volcano, is the sacred resting ground of the Ibaloi people and other Indigenous groups. Their dead are mummified and buried in caves on the mountain. Despite this sanctity, and the site being designated a national park, illegal logging and burning for conversion to agriculture continues to put pressure on the forests of Mount Pulag. Many of the surrounding – less sacred – mountains are already devoid of montane forest.

Rhododendron taxifolium was first introduced into cultivation by the Royal Botanic Garden Edinburgh in 1992, after we were given permission by the National Museum in Manila to distribute the species for conservation purposes and to establish an *ex-situ* conservation collection. The species now grows at more than eight *ex-situ* sites, and is a priority species for the Global Conservation Consortium for *Rhododendron*, established by Botanic Gardens Conservation International in 2018 and coordinated by the Royal Botanic Garden Edinburgh.

> *At home on a sacred mountain, burial place of the famous Kabayan fire mummies for more than 3,000 years.*

The Global Conservation Consortium for *Rhododendron* currently comprises experts from 16 institutions including botanic gardens with diverse *Rhododendron* collections in Europe, the USA, Canada, New Zealand and Australia, along with botanical institutions in the centres of *Rhododendron* diversity in China, India, Indonesia, Nepal and Papua New Guinea. They work together to prioritise conservation action, coordinate *ex-situ* conservation collections, and build capacity for effective *in-situ* conservation of this iconic plant group.

Specimen notes | Grown from cuttings taken by the Royal Botanic Garden Edinburgh's George Argent in the Philippines in 1992.

Location | Edinburgh (Glasshouses).

Conservation status | `CR`

Retrophyllum minus

Retrophyllum minus – bois bouchon or the corkwood tree – is a small conifer in the entirely southern hemisphere family Podocarpaceae. It is found only in New Caledonia, a focus of the Royal Botanic Garden Edinburgh's conifer research for over two decades, and home to more than 40 unique conifer species.

The corkwood tree is tiny for a conifer, reaching only two to three metres tall, and grows either in shallow flowing streams or at the water's edge. When mature, the base of the trunk is flared, giving it the appearance of a miniature baobab!

Member of a conifer family once widespread over the southern supercontinent of Gondwanaland.

The tree's bark is rough and fissured, and its branches short and stout, forming an irregular crown. The narrow leaves are arranged in a spiral and twisted at the base so that alternate leaves point in opposite directions – the origin of the name *Retrophyllum*. Its fruits are pear-shaped and maroon when ripe.

Although it is constantly inundated with water, it does not have the pneumatophores (aerial roots specialised for exchanging gases, colloquially called 'knees') that characterise other wetland conifers such as *Taxodium* (swamp cypress). Instead, small air channels within the stem transport gases to and from the roots and other submerged parts of the tree – these channels in the wood are the source of its common name, corkwood.

The corkwood tree is known from only a few sites in the south of New Caledonia's largest island, Grand Terre, with a total population of around 2,500 individuals.

The construction of dams associated with nickel mining, changes in water levels, and severe wildfires that rage through the *maquis*-type (shrubland) vegetation all continue to threaten the species.

Fortunately, it is relatively easy to grow from both seeds and cuttings. Active conservation projects are underway in New Caledonia, as well as *ex-situ* programmes at botanic gardens around the world.

Specimen notes | Grown from seed collected in New Caledonia by the International Conifer Conservation Programme in 1999. Extracted DNA is also stored in the Royal Botanic Garden Edinburgh's germplasm repository.

Location | Edinburgh (Glasshouses).

Conservation status | EN

Tahina spectabilis

First scientifically described in 2008, *Tahina spectabilis* (Arecaceae) was then known only from a single, small, remote site in Analalava district of north-west Madagascar, where around 30 mature trees remain.

The largest palm to grow naturally on Madagascar, *T. spectabilis* is monocarpic just like our dwarf cowhorn agave and *Meconopsis superba*. Individuals live for an estimated 50 years, sending up one enormous flowering spike before dying. In fact, the species is often called the 'suicide palm'.

Tahina spectabilis is the only species in the genus *Tahina*, a Malagasy word which means 'protected' or 'blessed', and is the given name of Anne-Tahina Metz, daughter of the discoverer of the tahina palm. The epithet *spectabilis* is from the Latin for 'spectacular'.

Within the palm family, *Tahina* is classified in the tribe Chuniophoeniceae, a bizarrely diverse and geographically widespread group containing *Nannorrhops* in Arabia, Iran, Afghanistan and Pakistan, *Kerriodoxa* of southern Thailand, *Chuniophoenix* from Vietnam, southern China and Hainan, and Madagascar's *Tahina*.

The species' natural extent within Madagascar is unknown, but it is likely to have been reduced by agricultural conversion. It is now threatened by fires, which are increasingly frequent due to changes in land use, and grazing, which reduces the quality of its habitat and hinders regeneration. Research and conservation work are ongoing: in 2017, an expedition by the Royal Botanic Gardens, Kew, found a new population of 27 individuals, effectively doubling the documented number of wild suicide palms.

Seeds of *T. spectabilis* were sent to Kew's Millennium Seed Bank in 2008 and passed from there to 11 other botanic gardens. It is likely that the Royal Botanic Garden Edinburgh's plant originates from these seeds.

> *One of the top 10 species discoveries of 2008, according to the International Institute for Species Exploration.*

Specimen notes | From seed collected in Madagascar.

Location | Edinburgh (not on public display).

Conservation status | CR

Pyrus korshinskyi

The ancient fruit-and-nut forests of Central Asia are home to the living ancestors of many domesticated fruit trees, including apple, apricot, pear and walnut. Unsustainable grazing, cutting and firewood collection have reduced these rich forests to just 10 per cent of their original range.

One of the casualties of this habitat loss is *Pyrus korshinskyi* (Rosaceae) – the Kazak, or Bukharan, pear. Native to Kyrgyzstan, Tajikistan, Uzbekistan and possibly Afghanistan, in the wild it is now restricted to a tiny, fragmented population in relatively inaccessible locations.

> *The largest cultivated Kazak pear tree in the world is found in Edinburgh.*

Protecting species of crop wild relatives like the Kazak pear is of global importance, as they provide important sources of genetic diversity to help maintain food security. This is by providing resistance against disease or other environmental stresses, particularly those caused by a rapidly changing climate.

When the Kazak pear was last assessed in 2007, its habitat was still shrinking and its numbers declining due to multiple threats including overgrazing by cattle, overharvesting of fruit for consumption and local sale, and collection of saplings for use as grafting rootstocks.

Remnant populations remain within three nature reserves in Tajikistan, including the Dashtijum and Childuktaron reserves, where the Royal Botanic Garden Edinburgh runs a capacity-building project focused on local crop species with horticulturalists at Kulob Botanic Garden. Fauna and Flora International are also working here to replant groves of *P. korshinskyi*.

The Kazak pear tree at the Royal Botanic Garden Edinburgh is listed on the *Tree Register of the British Isles* as a Champion Tree – the largest Kazak pear in cultivation. It was last measured in 2004 at eight metres tall with a trunk girth of 1.26 metres. It is quite spectacular in spring when covered in white blossom and, at over 50 years old, its gnarled branches are a great place for spotting lichens.

Specimen notes | Two trees, at Edinburgh and at Benmore, stem from the same plant received in 1969.

Location | Benmore; Edinburgh (*Pyrus* Lawn).

Conservation status | CR

Dracaena serrulata

Dracaena serrulata (Ruscaceae – butcher's broom family) – in Arabic *ayrob* or in English the Arabian dragon tree – is one of a genus of around 80 species, the best-known being *D. draco* (Canary Islands dragon tree). Only a few *Dracaena* grow as trees; most are succulent shrubs. The Arabian dragon tree grows to around five metres tall, with a distinctive umbrella-shaped crown, and is found in drier areas of the escarpment mountains of southern Oman and Yemen.

Many *Dracaena* – including this one – are valued for their red resin, which is used as a pigment and medicine. In southern Oman, fibres extracted from the stiff leaves are twisted or plaited into ropes with a variety of cultural uses, from securing people over cliffs to collect wild honey, to making pulleys for lowering heavy loads of frankincense resin to waiting camel trains.

Most of our western knowledge of the Arabian dragon tree stems from work done by the Royal Botanic Garden Edinburgh's Tony Miller with linguist Miranda Morris in the 1980s, documenting the flora and its uses for the Sultan of Oman, in the epic *Plants of Dhofar*. Some taxonomic confusion remains surrounding the identity of Arabian *Dracaena* species, and work is ongoing to confirm their identities. At present, we recognise *D. serrulata* in the south of Oman and Yemen as separate from *D. ombet* in north-west Yemen and western Saudi Arabia.

Specimen notes | Collected in May 1985, near Jibjat in Dhofar, southern Oman.

Location | Edinburgh (Glasshouses).

Conservation status | EN

Today, *D. serrulata* is suffering a serious decline in numbers and in habitat quality, and has very low levels of regeneration. Studies suggest that it does best where it is covered by fog during the monsoon season: the structure of the trees' crown is thought to be effective at capturing the fog's moisture. It is likely that disruption of Southern Arabia's annual monsoon has contributed to the loss of Arabian dragon trees.

Ropes made from Dracaena serrulata leaves are integral to cultural activities such as collecting honey and harvesting frankincense.

The *Dracaena* of Arabia and Soqotra are iconic plants and flagship taxa for conservation. The Royal Botanic Garden Edinburgh has been working with Oman Botanic Garden to rescue trees threatened by development and translocate them to the Garden, in Muscat. The work has been very successful, resulting in a large collection of *Dracaena* which will be used both to secure the future of the species, and to create a Glasshouse display to educate and inspire garden visitors.

Acer griseum

With its beautiful bark and spectacular autumn foliage, the Chinese paperbark maple, *Acer griseum* (Sapindaceae – soapberry family) is widely cultivated as an ornamental and street tree. In the wild it occurs only in China, where it is known as 血皮枫 (*xue pi feng*).

The paperbark maple was first introduced to Europe by Veitch and Sons of Chelsea – at the time Europe's largest family-run nursery, and sponsors of prolific plant collector Ernest Henry Wilson's first expedition to China in 1902. Wilson later sent a pair of seedlings to the USA's Arnold Arboretum, Boston, in 1907, from which most – if not all – of North America's ornamental paperbark maples are descended. In the UK, the species has received a Royal Horticultural Society Award of Garden Merit.

Paper bark and helicopter fruits.

Though the paperbark maple is widely distributed across China, the trees are isolated in severely fragmented populations – each generally fewer than 10 individuals, with the total wild population likely fewer than 250 trees.

The species is cut for firewood, even within protected areas, and sometimes coppiced – a practice which may prevent trees from flowering, fruiting and therefore reproducing. This is compounded by competition from surrounding species.

Although the paperbark maple can be found in almost 200 botanic gardens around the world, the genetic diversity, and therefore conservation potential, of these collections is unclear. It is likely that all cultivated plants – including those at the Royal Botanic Garden Edinburgh – stem from a few early twentieth-century introductions.

In 2015, the North America-China Plant Exploration Consortium instigated a collaborative, targeted collecting expedition for the paperbark maple, with the aim of enhancing the genetic diversity in cultivation. They managed to sample 66 trees, several of which are now growing in the Arnold Arboretum and elsewhere.

Specimen notes | Multiple from cultivated material. Our oldest, dating from 1938, was bequeathed by Admiral Sir Archibald Berkeley Milne (1855–1938), from his estate at Inveresk Gate, Musselburgh, East Lothian.

Location | Benmore (several sites – even in the car park!); Dawyck; Edinburgh (several sites including Chinese Hillside).

Conservation status |

Eucalyptus morrisbyi

Eucalyptus morrisbyi (Morrisby's gum; Myrtaceae) is unique to Tasmania and confined to two small localities in the south-east of the island. As with other *Eucalyptus* species, it is culturally significant to, and widely used by, the island's Indigenous people.

Described scientifically by local schoolteacher Robert Brett (1898–1975) in 1939, it is thought to be named for John Robert Morrisby (1832–1923), who supplemented naturally grown trees with an avenue of the species at his family farm near Hobart. The Morrisbys still farm in the area to this day.

Though widely planted as ornamentals, Morrisby's gum is considered functionally near-extinct in the wild, with fewer than 30 reproductive individuals remaining, many of which are in poor condition.

The disastrous decline of the species is attributed largely to land clearance for agriculture, with the remaining trees damaged by vertebrates (possums and wallabies) and invertebrates (such as autumn gum moth – *Mnesampela privata*). This is exacerbated by climate-change-induced drought conditions. Once stressed, for example by drought, the trees are very susceptible to herbivory (being eaten), which can cause enough damage to be fatal.

Regeneration has been hampered by weeds, such as the hemiparasitic (able to photosynthesise but also receive nutrients from its host) vine *Cassytha pubescens* (devil's twine), and introduced *Nassella trichotoma* (serrated tussock grass). Changes to fire regimes may also have an impact here: while fire is required to stimulate the seed capsules to release their seed – and capsules are only viable for around two years – fire can also kill young saplings.

Conservation in a race against climate change.

The remaining stands of this *Eucalyptus* are now protected within nature reserves, where targeted recovery efforts are ongoing, including the removal of invasive exotic species, fencing to exclude browsing animals, and supplementary planting. Four *ex-situ* subpopulations were established in Tasmania in the 1990s, with relatively high survival rates. Conservationists aim to maintain genetic diversity through *ex-situ* planting and seed banking from natural stands, and ultimately to introduce the species to new localities likely to maintain a suitable climate in the face of future climate change. The question is – will they be too late?

Specimen notes | Three trees, one grown from Tasmanian seed in 2011, the other two obtained from the Howick Estate, Northumberland, in 2017.

Location | Logan (Tasmanian Creek and elsewhere).

Conservation status | CR

Hibiscus clayi

Hibiscus clayi (Malvaceae) is known in Hawaiian as *koki'o'ula* – *'ula* meaning red as it also does in *Abutilon menziesii.* A compact shrub with spectacular red flowers almost all year round, its convenient size and good looks make it a popular choice locally for gardens and containers.

In the wild, *koki'o'ula* has been recorded at just two sites in the Nounou mountains on the island of Kaua'i, where there are thought to be only 111 individuals remaining, with numbers still trending downwards.

> *Nearly 90 per cent of Hawaii's plants are found nowhere else on Earth.*

The Hawaiian Islands are rich in endemic species, with nearly 90 per cent of their plants found nowhere else in the world. *Hibiscus* is no exception: Hawaii boasts six native species – including the islands' state flower *Hibiscus brackenridgei* (*ma'o hau hele*) – all but one of them unique to the archipelago. They are traditionally used for ornamental purposes such as making leis, and the beautiful blooms are pollinated by birds.

In 1928, local forester Albert Walter Duvel (1903–1978) spotted several unusual, small *Hibiscus* plants on Kaua'i that had been trampled by cattle. He brought them into cultivation, where they grew to be unlike any species previously recorded. They were finally described by a husband-and-wife team,

botanists Otto (1899–1988) and Isa Degener (1924–2018) in 1959. The species was named for popular horticulturalist and instructor of botany at Leeward Community College on O'ahu, Horace F. Clay, author of *Hawaii Garden Tropical Exotics* and *Hawaii Garden Tropical Shrubs*.

Koki'o'ula is protected under the US Plant Extinction Prevention Program, and the National Tropical Botanic Garden – located in Florida and Hawaii – maintains both living and seed collections to act as insurance against extinction in the wild. Experimental reintroductions to bolster wild populations are being carried out and monitored by the National Tropical Botanic Garden.

Specimen notes | Grown from seed collected in Hawaii and brought to the Royal Botanic Garden Edinburgh in 1959 by Austrian-American botanist and ethnographer Joseph Rock (1884–1962).

Location | Edinburgh (Glasshouses).

Conservation status | CR

Nothofagus alessandrii

Nothofagus alessandrii (Nothofagaceae – southern beech family) is found only in south-central Chile where it is known as *ruil*. One of 11 species of *Nothofagus* in the country, it is among Chile's most threatened trees and, in autumn when the leaves turn, one of the most handsome.

Restricted to the temperate rainforests of the coastal cordillera, the species' population has been dramatically reduced by overexploitation, both for fuelwood and for its high-quality and highly desirable timber, and by habitat loss including that caused by introduced pine plantations. The coastal area of south-central Chile has seen some of the world's highest rates of deforestation in modern times.

Specimen notes | Collected in Chile as seedlings or young plants since 2008. Most have been sent to safe sites around the British Isles, but a few remain at the Royal Botanic Garden Edinburgh.

Location | Benmore (Chilean Rainforest Glade); Edinburgh (Experimental Garden); Logan.

Conservation status |

Only 15 highly fragmented populations are now thought to remain, covering an area of just 3.5 square kilometres. Fire is an increasing threat, and in 2017 many trees were lost in the country's worst wildfires, which displaced thousands of people and killed 11.

Fiery autumn colour, imperilled by wildfires.

Nothofagus alessandrii is protected in Chile in one important reserve which is named after the species: Parque Nacional Los Ruiles. Outside the country, the Royal Botanic Garden Edinburgh carried out the first successful introductions of the species in 2008, is working to increase the genetic diversity of trees in *ex-situ* cultivation, and has distributed more than 100 trees to 45 sites across the UK and Ireland.

Lodoicea maldivica

Lodoicea maldivica (Arecaceae), the *coco de mer* or, more prosaically, double coconut, is the only species of *Lodoicea*. It is famous for its enormous seed which, at 18 kilograms, is the heaviest and most valuable in the world, and an example of 'island gigantism', a phenomenon in which plants and animals from isolated islands tend to grow particularly large.

Restricted to just two small islands in the Seychelles, *coco de mer* trees grow up to 30 metres tall with leaves up to 10 metres long, ideal for thatching. Locally, the fruits were once used as bowls and for bailing out boats, but in the sixteenth century they became traded throughout the world for their ornamental value and perceived medicinal powers, based – following the 'doctrine of signatures' – on the suggestive shape of the nuts.

Seychelles legend tells that on stormy nights, male coco de mer trees become mobile, walking to the waiting females to reproduce, and that any witnesses will suffer certain death.

For centuries, the source of these marvellous nuts – which from time to time washed up on beaches around the world – was a mystery. Many believed they were produced by a submarine species, which explains the name *coco de mer*. They were eventually traced to the Seychelles by the 1768 expedition of French *chevalier* Marc-Joseph Marion du Fresne (1724–1772). Du Fresne's success was short-lived, as his second-in-command returned to Praslin in 1769 and exported such a huge quantity of nuts that he flooded and practically destroyed the market.

The *coco de mer* is a keystone species, supporting many animals unique to the Seychelles, including the vulnerable Seychelles black parrot (*Coracopsis barklyi*). The largest population, in the Vallée de Mai on the island of Praslin, is designated a UNESCO World Heritage Site. However, the species remains hugely threatened by overexploitation, fire, land clearance, competition from introduced species, and poor rates of regeneration. Its complex reproductive biology is still shrouded in mystery, hindering *ex-situ* cultivation efforts.

As we learn more about the *coco de mer*'s requirements, cultivation at botanic gardens around the world is increasingly successful. At the Royal Botanic Garden Edinburgh we have successfully germinated and grown on a plant, which at time of publication had reached 16 years old. A new local scheme, whereby residents plant trees on their land, is in its infancy but so far hugely popular.

Specimen notes | Grown from a seed received from the Vallée de Mai, courtesy of the Seychelles Islands Foundation, in 2005.

Location | Edinburgh (Glasshouses).

Conservation status | EN

Acer pentaphyllum

Acer pentaphyllum (Sapindaceae) – 五小叶枫 (*wu xiao ye feng*), the Chinese maple or five-lobe maple – is found only in the watershed of the Yalong Jiang, a tributary of the Chang Jiang (Yangtze) in south-west Sichuan, China. It is named for its deeply incised, five-lobed leaves.

The species was introduced to the west by Joseph Rock in 1929 via Hilliers' nursery which, founded in 1864 in Winchester, is now one of the largest nurseries in the UK. Trees from Rock's introduction still survive at the Strybing Arboretum in Golden Gate Park, San Francisco, USA.

In the wild, the five-lobe maple is currently known from only four sites, with a total of perhaps 500 individuals. Twenty-five per cent of the plants are recorded as having been lost in a single generation, and an 80 per cent loss is predicted over three.

The many threats to this species include overgrazing by goats, sheep and cattle, overharvesting for firewood, road construction and dam construction. Indeed, a damning 2018 IUCN assessment states that, "the construction of a dam, or the occurrence of fire, or a large landslide could destroy all individuals of the tree in one go".

This is not idle speculation, as the Yalong Jiang is being heavily developed for hydroelectric power.

> *The rarest maple on Earth.*

One population of *A. pentaphyllum* has already been lost to a power plant, and more dams are planned or under construction.

In the wild, local scientists believe that public outreach alongside political influence, national protection and an integrated conservation plan will all have to come together if we are to save this species.

However, there is hope. The China Biodiversity Conservation and Green Development Foundation has established *ex-situ* conservation sites at three locations in Tianshui, Lanzhou and Xing'an Meng. Although regeneration is poor, multiple trees are producing viable seeds which have been propagated *ex situ* over several years and are now growing at nearly 50 botanic gardens in China and around the world.

Specimen notes | Three young trees grown from collections made in Sichuan in 2010, obtained via Bedgebury National Pinetum.

Location | Edinburgh (Chinese Hillside).

Conservation status |

Picea omorika

Restricted to Serbia, and Bosnia and Herzegovina, *Picea omorika*, the rare Serbian spruce (Pinaceae), was first discovered in 1875 by botanist Josif Pančić (1814–1888) in Serbia's Tara Mountains – now a national park. The trees occur on steep, north-facing limestone slopes.

This is a very distinctive conifer, forming exceptionally narrow, conical trees up to 30 metres tall. The epithet *omorika* comes from the Serbian word for spruce, and has come to symbolise slenderness in local culture. In fact, the spruces are so slim – with narrow, downward-pointing branches and cones borne inconveniently at the very top – that Royal

> *This conifer does not make life easy for botanists.*

Botanic Garden Edinburgh botanists were unable to climb them to collect seed. Instead, they had to scale the adjacent rockface and lasso the tops of the trees, pulling them down to extract seed from the cones.

The species may be outcompeted by other trees, but the main threat to the Serbian spruce is fire. In 2021, wildfires in Bosnia and Herzegovina destroyed 80 per cent of the largest population at Veliki Stolac – a single event which may have catapulted the species from endangered to critically endangered.

Working with local partners, scientists from the Royal Botanic Garden Edinburgh's International Conifer Conservation Programme have collected seed from across the Serbian spruce's range, including the devastated Veliki Stolac population, and propagated almost 1,000 trees, which are now planted at safe sites across the UK and Ireland.

Specimen notes | The earliest introduction to Edinburgh was in 1957, but this was not of known wild origin. Hundreds more trees have been propagated from seed since 1991 and are growing at safe sites around the British Isles.

Location | Benmore; Dawyck; Edinburgh.

Conservation status | EN

Musa coccinea

The natural range of *Musa coccinea* (Musaceae – banana family) – 红蕉 (*hóng jiāo*) or the scarlet banana – is thought to have once extended across a large part of southern China and Vietnam. Today, it is considered extinct in the wild in China and restricted to just three, widely separated localities in Vietnam.

The species may be a victim of its own beauty. With a Royal Horticultural Society Award of Garden Merit in the UK, it is one of the best-suited bananas to ornamental growing due to its small size and eye-catching red inflorescences, intricately adapted to bat pollination. In its natural range, high horticultural demand is suspected to have led to significant over-collection. More research is urgently needed to confirm the remaining wild distribution of scarlet bananas, the status of existing wild populations, and the threats which are contributing to its decline.

The scarlet banana is also found as an introduced species in Costa Rica, Java, Trinidad and Tobago, and the Philippines.

With very limited genetic diversity in cultivation, bananas (including plantains) are one of the world's most at-risk crops. As important crop wild relatives, with the potential to contribute traits such as disease tolerance or drought resistance, the whole banana genus (*Musa*) is listed on the UN Food and Agriculture Organization's International Treaty on Plant Genetic Resources for Food and Agriculture. This treaty supports sustainable agriculture, food security, and fair and equitable benefit-sharing of crops and crop wild relatives. The 148 signatories share a global pool of genetic resources for 64 of our most important crops – together accounting for 80 per cent of global nutrition – which may be accessed for research, breeding and training, and commit to the rights of farmers and principles of sustainable use.

An important wild relative of the staple food crop.

At time of writing, Botanic Gardens Conservation International recorded 37 botanic gardens growing the scarlet banana, and four separate wild-origin samples of genetic material – one held at the Royal Botanic Gardens, Kew's Millennium Seed Bank in Wakehurst, Kent, and three at the Biodiversity International *Musa* Germplasm Transit Centre in Leuven, Belgium, home to the world's largest collection of banana germplasm (living material such as seeds or tissue).

Specimen notes | One plant obtained from the Royal Botanic Gardens, Kew in 1977; another by George Argent from Tenom Agricultural Station, Sabah, Malaysia, in 1990 – both of cultivated origin.

Location | Edinburgh (Glasshouses).

Conservation status | EN

Echium pininana

Echium pininana (Boraginaceae – forget-me-not family) – giant viper's bugloss, tree echium or tower of jewels – is found wild only in the mountains of north-east La Palma in the Canary Islands.

The giant viper's bugloss is so far known from seven sites on La Palma. It is widespread in cultivation as an ornamental, and has become naturalised in California and in the warmer southern and western parts of the UK – particularly the Isle of Wight and Channel Islands – where it grows in large thickets. At the Royal Botanic Garden Edinburgh's own tropical paradise, Logan Botanic Garden, the tall flowering spikes are a regular spectacle, even where they haven't intentionally been planted.

An enormous relative of our humble borage – and just as popular with the bees.

Like many island species, the *Echium* of the Canary Islands tend to be larger and woodier than their mainland counterparts. The huge flowering spikes of *E. pininana* – often several metres tall – suggest an evolutionary adaptation to obtain sufficient sunlight in the forest gaps where it grows. In common with several other species in this book, and three other Canary Island *Echium* species, the giant viper's bugloss is monocarpic. Each plant grows for just two years, sending up its huge flowering spike in its second year before dying.

Like *Polystichum drepanum* and *Isoplexis sceptrum*, *E. pininana* is a species of the once-widespread Mediterranean *laurisilva* (laurel forests), now mostly restricted to the Azores, Madeira and the Canary Islands. The *laurisilva* survives here due to a combination of climatic conditions at a latitude that would otherwise be too dry to sustain it. In the near future, as climate change disrupts these weather patterns, the *laurisilva* may be wiped out, along with *E. pininana* and all the other flora and fauna unique to this ancient ecosystem.

Specimen notes | Original plants obtained when Logan came into the hands of the Royal Botanic Garden Edinburgh in 1969. The species frequently pops up where it has not been planted!

Location | Logan (Terrace and East Border).

Conservation status | EN

Dicksonia arborescens

Our second St Helena endemic, *Dicksonia arborescens* (St Helena tree fern; Dicksoniaceae – tree fern family) dominates the mountain cloud forests along the island's central ridge and highest point, Diana's Peak. At up to four metres tall, the plants' flexible stems allow them to withstand high winds where other species might not survive.

In the past, the species was also widespread at lower altitudes, but these were cleared for agriculture, first as pasture, then for cultivation of *Phormium tenax* (New Zealand flax), a mainstay of St Helena's economy in the first half of the twentieth century.

Specimen notes | Our older tree fern was grown from wild spores collected in 2000 on St Helena, another was propagated from spores of that plant in 2013.

Location | Edinburgh (Glasshouses).

Conservation status | VU

Though occupying a very small proportion of the total land mass, the tree fern is vital to the ecology of the island, playing a major role in water retention. The great surface area of the highly divided leaves captures moisture from mist, and decaying leaves below the plants store run-off. The soil under tree fern stands has been found to contain almost twice as much water as that under adjoining flax plantations. Thickets of St Helena tree fern now constitute one of the few remaining natural ecosystems on the island.

> *Tree fern thickets are vital to water cycling on this exposed island.*

The St Helena tree fern is slow to mature and slow to regenerate. The tiny gametophytes – the plants' sexual stage – require constant moisture and bare earth to grow on, conditions which are nowadays becoming rare due to introduced weed species. Young ferns do sometimes manage to establish on roadsides but are usually weeded out before they reach maturity.

In 1996, the area around Diana's Peak was designated St Helena's first national park, and the tree fern is protected under the National Conservation Area development plans. *Ex-situ* conservation in botanic gardens, however, remains an important way to protect the species from extinction, and the Royal Botanic Garden Edinburgh is one of few sites to grow the St Helena tree fern.

Valdivia gayana

Valdivia gayana (Escalloniaceae) is known in Chile as *planta del león* (lion plant). A small shrub, it bears large clusters of incredibly bright magenta flowers – their colour really has to be seen to be believed.

Valdivia gayana is the only species of *Valdivia,* which like many Chilean plants was named for Spanish *conquistador* Pedro Gutiérrez de Valdivia (1497–1553), the first Royal Governor of Chile.

> *It survived the world's worst recorded earthquake – can it survive our destruction of its habitat?*

Though it has not yet been evaluated by the IUCN, *V. gayana* meets the internationally recognised criteria for endangered status. The main threat to the species is habitat loss, as much of its natural habitat has been converted to commercial plantations.

The species is now confined in the wild to rocky outcrops in shady forested coastal slopes to the south of the country, around the city of Valdivia, also named for the same *conquistador*. One such site lies at the Gruta de la Aguada, a cave holding a shrine to the Virgin Mary, close to the fishing town of Corral. The religious nature of the site has helped to protect the plant at this location.

In 1960, Valdivia and surrounding areas were devastated by the most powerful earthquake ever recorded, measuring 9.5 on the Richter scale. The force was so strong that it caused a ferocious tsunami with waves up to 10 metres high, which decimated the coastline of Corral. Unlike over 1,000 people who lost their lives, the *planta del león* was lucky to survive.

Like several of our species, *V. gayana* was introduced into cultivation through Veitch and Sons – this time through their Exeter nursery. They first exhibited a flowering plant at the Royal Horticultural Society in London in 1863, where it received a commendation.

At the Royal Botanic Garden Edinburgh, the species is cultivated from plants introduced in 2012 by Chilean specialist Martin Gardner. Our horticulturists have carried out intensive research to understand better how to propagate and cultivate the *planta del león*, to ensure its continued survival.

Specimen notes | Grown from collections made in Chile in 2006 and 2012, plus a youngster grown from seed of the 2012 collection in 2015.

Location | Benmore (Fernery); Edinburgh (Glasshouses); Logan (outside).

Conservation status | EN (proposed)

Glyptostrobus pensilis

Known in China as 水松 (*shuî sōng*), in Vietnam as *thông nuóc*, *thuy tùng* or *h'ral*, in Lao as *mai hing sam*, and elsewhere as the water pine or Chinese swamp cypress, *Glyptostrobus pensilis* (Cupressaceae) is the only remaining species in a genus of conifers once found throughout the northern hemisphere.

Over the past 100 million years, its distribution has expanded and contracted until now it is known only from southern China, two degraded swamps in Vietnam, and a few, recently discovered stands in a remote part of central Laos. Its tale is one of repeated cycles of disappointment and hope.

The Chinese swamp cypress grows only in flat, wet, swampy areas, which – unfortunately for the tree – are also ideal for rice cultivation. Conversion of forested land to rice fields has been one of the main drivers of its decline, especially in China.

In Laos, *G. pensilis* trees were first located in 2007, during a survey prior to the construction of the Nam Theun 2 hydroelectric scheme. These were inundated and lost when the reservoir was flooded, and although some seed was collected, it failed to germinate. A few additional stands around the reservoir were also destroyed in the process of converting swamps to much-needed paddy fields.

Between 2013 and 2017, a series of expeditions by multinational teams including scientists from the Royal Botanic Garden Edinburgh located two old-growth stands in the hills that make up the watershed above the reservoir, comprising several hundred large trees, some in excess of 900 years old. Tragically, by 2018 almost all the trees in one stand were illegally felled for the furniture trade, leaving only one surviving old-growth stand.

The only living species of a once widespread, majestic genus.

In collaboration with local people, protected area staff and collaborators from San Francisco and New York, a concerted conservation programme was initiated, including establishing a small nursery where several thousand young trees have been propagated to be planted back into the wild.

In the late 2010s, work on populations in Fujian and Hong Kong determined that these may also represent additional wild stands, rather than cultivated or naturalised as previously thought. It is now likely that the Chinese swamp cypress will be re-assessed as endangered rather than critically endangered – things are slowly looking up for this ancient giant.

Specimen notes | Several plants collected in China in the 1970s and one wild-origin plant from Vietnam grafted onto a swamp cypress (*Taxodium distichum*) rootstock.

Location | Edinburgh (Glasshouses); Logan (outside).

Conservation status | CR

Eucalyptus gunnii

Eucalyptus gunnii, the cider gum, is – like *E. morrisbyi* – exclusive to Tasmania and culturally significant to and widely used by the Indigenous Palawa people. The cider gum's sap is traditionally used to make a cider-like fermented drink called *way-a-linah*, explaining the tree's common name. The leaves of *E. gunnii* also produce essential oils, which are widely used to treat respiratory illnesses and as an antiseptic.

The cider gum was formally described in 1844 by British botanist Joseph Dalton Hooker (1817–1911), who later became Director of the Royal Botanic Gardens, Kew. It was named for the collector, Ronald Campbell Gunn (1803–1881), a South African-born Australian politician and botanist.

> *Source of a traditional drink which is undergoing a revival in popularity in its homeland.*

Eucalyptus gunnii is considered the most frost-tolerant species of *Eucalyptus* and, as such, is the most widely planted *Eucalyptus* in the UK, holding a Royal Horticultural Society Award of Garden Merit for its ornamental qualities. However, the tree can grow to a great height, and do so very quickly, so care needs to be taken when planting it in a domestic garden. With judicious and consistent pruning, it can be successfully sustained as a shrub – a process which also maintains the round-leaved juvenile foliage rather than the narrow-leaved adult form.

The cider gum is remarkably adapted to survive periodic fires. At the base of the trunk it produces a 'lignotuber' – a woody swelling of the root crown containing buds and starch stores. If the main stem is destroyed, these buds can regrow, supported by their starch stores, until leaves develop to allow photosynthesis to resume.

The wild population of *Eucalyptus gunnii* has decreased substantially in recent years, a decline which has been linked to climate change. More severe droughts, changing seasonality of rainfall, and increased maximum temperatures are all thought to be part of the puzzle. The trees also struggle to regenerate due to grazing and possum browsing. Although this widely planted species is never likely to become extinct, further restoration may be needed for it to survive in its natural range.

Specimen notes | Our oldest tree at Edinburgh was obtained from the Forestry Commission in 1964. Our only wild-origin collection can be found at Logan and was supplied as seed from Tasmania by Australia's Commonwealth Scientific and Industrial Research Organisation in 1985.

Location | Edinburgh (*Rhododendron* Walk); Logan (multiple sites).

Conservation status | EN

Franklinia alatamaha

22

The Franklin tree, *Franklinia alatamaha* (Theaceae) – named for US statesman Benjamin Franklin (1706–1790) – is the only known species of *Franklinia*, and is extinct in the wild.

Franklinia alatamaha was first brought to the attention of Europeans by naturalist William Bartram (1739–1823) during several collecting expeditions between 1765 and 1773. Although Bartram recorded it as "plentiful", he only ever located a single population, covering perhaps one hectare alongside the Altamaha River in Georgia, USA.

Bartram cultivated the plant from seed with his father, John (1699–1777), a good friend of Benjamin Franklin, and King George III's 'Royal Botanist for North America'. Their garden in Philadelphia is now the oldest surviving botanic garden in the nation. *Franklinia alatamaha* finally flowered in cultivation here in 1781. William Bartram's 1788 painting of the species hangs in the Natural History Museum in London.

All the Franklin trees in the world today are thought to be descended from the seed collected and cultivated by the Bartrams. The oldest examples may be seen at the Arnold Arboretum in Boston. It is an understandably popular ornamental, with fragrant, white flowers similar to single white *Camellia* blossoms, and bright autumn foliage.

The Franklin tree has not been seen in the wild since 1803, when it was last recorded by Scottish botanist John Lyon (1765–1814). The reasons for its extinction are unclear, but may include burning and clearing of land during early settlement, subsequent flooding, fungal diseases introduced via cotton plantations, and over-collection to meet horticultural demands in Europe in the late 1700s.

> *Shrouded in mystery, the true origins of this beautiful tree may never be understood.*

The species seems to have been on the brink of extinction even before Europeans arrived in the Americas; perhaps as a remnant of a colder-adapted forest species all but wiped out by glaciation and clinging on in a less-than-ideal southern part of its range. Some believe it was never native to Georgia at all, conceivably having grown from seed dropped by a passing migratory bird. The species lives on in thousands of plants grown at more than 100 botanic gardens around the world.

Specimen notes | Logan's plant was obtained from the Royal Botanic Gardens, Kew in 2016. Edinburgh's was grown from tissue culture and donated by the University of Georgia in 2018.

Location | Edinburgh (not on public display); Logan.

Conservation status | EW

Melampyrum sylvaticum

Nationally endangered, *Melampyrum sylvaticum* (the small cow-wheat; Orobanchaceae – broomrape family) is described by Royal Botanic Garden Edinburgh horticulturist Martine Borge, who specialises in rare Scottish species, as a 'Goldilocks plant' – only happy when the conditions are 'just right'. It needs permanent moisture but not waterlogging, yet must be sheltered from direct rainfall. It likes the right amount of light; not too much and not too little. It requires a host plant to grow on, and is thought to be dependent upon wood ants to disperse its remarkably large seeds.

A hemiparasite, the small cow-wheat is usually found in the ground flora of upland birch (*Betula*) woods. Relatively widespread in Europe, in the UK it is largely confined to the Scottish Highlands, where 19 fragmented, isolated and vulnerable populations have been identified.

> *Scotland's 'Goldilocks species', for which everything has to be 'just right'.*

Here it is categorised as endangered, and listed on the UK Biodiversity Action Plan.

The small cow-wheat may be at risk from the expansion of dense forest vegetation – either through plantation forestry or the spread of introduced species such as *Rhododendron ponticum*. It may also be threatened by increased temperatures and atmospheric carbon dioxide concentration. As an annual plant, if seeds fail to germinate in a given year, the population can dwindle – and even become extinct – very quickly.

Rhiannon Crichton, a PhD student at the Royal Botanic Garden Edinburgh, studied the small cow-wheat in the early 2010s and suggests that habitat fragmentation has had negative impacts on both the number and genetic diversity of Scotland's plants. Reduced genetic diversity may render the species unable to adapt to future threats such as climate change or newly introduced pests or diseases, putting it at risk of extinction in the UK.

Both *in-situ* and *ex-situ* work is ongoing at the Royal Botanic Garden Edinburgh to maximise the diversity remaining, including cross-pollinating populations from different sites. Borge and her colleagues are experimenting with how best to germinate and propagate the species, with a view to bulking-up populations for future restoration work in the Highlands.

Specimen notes | This annual species is regrown from seed every year – our original seed being collected in Scotland.

Location | Edinburgh (Experimental Garden).

Conservation status | EN (UK)

Amburana cearensis

Amburana cearensis (Fabaceae) is found across a large part of South America, a distribution reflected in its wide variety of names: *amburana, angelim, baru, cabocla, cerejeira rajada, cheiro, cumaru, louro ingá* and many more. A tall deciduous tree, it grows in seasonally dry tropical forests such as Brazil's *caatinga*, shedding its compound leaves during the dry season.

Dry forests – a focus of the Royal Botanic Garden Edinburgh's research and conservation work – are among the most threatened in the world, with less than 10 per cent of their original extent remaining in many countries. The scattered distribution of *A. cearensis* among these forests may reflect previous drier climates during the ice ages of the Pleistocene Epoch, when these forests might have been more extensive.

Amburana trees can be identified by their remarkable, peeling, reddish bark and unusual, single-petalled flowers. Scientists at the Royal Botanic Garden Edinburgh are sequencing *amburana*'s genome in an attempt to understand the genetic basis underpinning how such flowers develop, which may provide wider insights into floral development.

The bark and seeds of *amburana* are rich in coumarin, a sweet-smelling chemical compound first isolated from the related tonka bean tree (*Dipteryx odorata*, known in French as *coumarou*). Coumarin probably protects the plant against insect attack, but is now also used in sweets, soaps, perfumes and medicines.

> *A sought-after timber tree from South America's threatened dry forests.*

Amburana is used traditionally to treat stomach infections and respiratory complaints, and to de-worm animals.

Amburana timber is of high quality and sought after for use in woodwork, fine furniture, sculptures, construction, carpentry, barrels and handicrafts. It is also very resistant to insect attack, and as a bonus is extremely fragrant. It is commonly used to make barrels for ageing *cachaça*, a spirit made from sugar cane and the most popular spirit in Brazil.

Exploitation for timber has been the greatest threat to *amburana*, with most stands of mature trees having been destroyed. However, with care this can be reversed. A large conservation project – entitled *Recaatingamento* – has cultivated more than 15,000 seedlings for the restoration of degraded forests in Brazil.

Specimen notes | Grown from seed collected by the Royal Botanic Garden Edinburgh's Samuel Bridgewater and Jimmy Ratter with J. Batista dos Santos in Brazil in 1998.

Location | Edinburgh (not on public display).

Conservation status |

Guaiacum officinale

The many names of *Guaiacum officinale* (Zygophyllaceae – caltrop family), among them roughbark, *palo santo* (Spanish for 'holy wood') and *lignum vitae* (from the Latin meaning 'wood of life'), hint at its widely reputed medicinal properties. International trade in roughbark really took off in the nineteenth century, primarily for the treatment of syphilis in Europe.

The roughbark tree is found across most of the Caribbean, including the Lesser and Greater Antilles, Colombia, Venezuela, Guyana, Suriname and Panama, and is cultivated as far afield as Florida and India.

> *The national flower of Jamaica's uses range from cricket balls to cancer screening.*

Roughbark has been exploited for timber for more than 500 years. The very hard, high-density, oily wood is ideal for construction machinery, cogs and ship propellers, pestles and mortars, and cricket balls. A resin called *guaiac*, extracted from the wood, is used to flavour drinks, ice cream, chewing gum and cakes, but you might be put off your dessert by the other main use of *guaiac* – in the '*guaiac* faecal occult blood test' – a screen for colorectal cancer. When mixed with hydrogen peroxide, *guaiac* resin turns blue in the presence of even small amounts of blood as it is oxidised by haemoglobin.

International trade in roughbark has declined since the early twentieth century, due to a combination of so few trees being left, national policies against felling in some countries, and alternative materials becoming available for many of its uses. Medicinal demand is now largely met by cultivated trees rather than harvesting from the wild.

However, the roughbark is slow-growing and, with remaining populations small and scattered, it is now close to extinction across most of its natural range. Since 1992 the species has been CITES-listed, but illegal trade is still thought to occur, with timber harvested in the Dominican Republic being transported to Haiti, which is not a CITES signatory.

It remains unclear whether the species' decline in the wild will continue, or if current conservation and trade limitations have done enough to stabilise the population. In cultivation, the species is secured in more than 40 botanic gardens around the world.

Specimen notes | Grown from seed collected in Puerto Rico, supplied by the University of Florida in 1982.

Location | Edinburgh (Glasshouses).

Conservation status | EN

18

Pritchardia affinis

Pritchardia affinis (Arecaceae), *lo'ulu* or the Kona fan palm, was once widely cultivated by Indigenous Hawaiians, making it almost impossible to determine its natural range. Before pigs and rats were brought to the Hawaiian Islands by Polynesians, it is believed to have grown in extensive groves around much of the archipelago.

The reasons for its extensive cultivation were multiple: the leaf blades were used for thatching, the wood for spears, and the seeds were eaten. From the nineteenth century onwards, the leaves were also made into hats. Older palms can often be found with footholds cut into the trunks for ease of harvesting leaves and fruits from these 25-metre-tall trees.

Having arrived in Hawaii more than 40,000 years ago, probably transported across the ocean by chance on rafts of debris, *lo'ulu* is now restricted to a small area, mostly around coastal settlements, of the district of South Kona on the leeward, western side of the Island of Hawaii. Only 50–60 trees remain in the wild, a number which is unlikely to increase while rats and pigs are around to eat the seeds and destroy any new growth.

Pigs and rats have a lot to answer for.

However, a habitat restoration project in the Hawaii Volcanoes National Park – centred around the active volcanoes of Kīlauea and Mauna Loa – is reintroducing *lo'ulu* to part of its natural range by cultivating the plants *ex situ*, and the species is grown at some 18 botanic gardens around the world including the Royal Botanic Garden Edinburgh.

Specimen notes | Received in 1967 from the Royal Botanic Gardens, Kew.

Location | Edinburgh (Glasshouses).

Conservation status | CR

Isoplexis sceptrum

A giant relative of the common foxglove (*Digitalis purpurea*), *Isoplexis sceptrum* (Plantaginaceae – plantain family), the Madeira foxglove, can grow up to four metres tall. As with *Echium pininana* and *Lodoicea maldivica*, its enormous size is considered an example of island gigantism.

Unique to the *laurisilva* forests of northern Madeira, and threatened by introduced invasive weeds such as Scotch broom (*Cytisus scoparius*) and black wattle (*Acacia mearnsii*) and by changing water catchments, there are thought to be between 250 and 1,000 mature individuals left, at fewer than five sites.

> *A giant version of our common foxglove, doing well in the climate of south-west Scotland.*

The entire wild population of the Madeira foxglove lies within the Parque Natural da Madeira, a UNESCO World Heritage Site and biogenetic reserve, and the world's largest surviving area of primary *laurisilva* (around 22,000 hectares). The Parque protects a highly specialised suite of flora and fauna including at least 76 plant species known from nowhere else in the world. Within the Parque, the Madeira foxglove has been observed to regenerate, and the wild population is now considered to be stable.

The Madeira foxglove makes an eye-catching ornamental, though rather difficult to grow, and is found in around 25 botanic gardens worldwide. It does well at our own Logan Botanic Garden, where it can be seen in flower throughout the summer.

Specimen notes | Logan's population derives from wild-collected seed obtained via the Royal Botanic Gardens, Kew in 1975, as well as a cultivated specimen received from Tresco Abbey Gardens in 2010.

Location | Logan (Terrace and East Border).

Conservation status | EN

Trochetiopsis ebenus

Another St Helena endemic, *Trochetiopsis ebenus* (Malvaceae), the St Helena, or dwarf, ebony was once believed to be extinct. In 1980, two plants were found on an inhospitable rock formation known as 'Lot, Lot's wife and the Asses' Ears', where they had escaped the attention of grazing animals.

The rediscoverers were St Helena botanist George Benjamin (1935–2012) and Quentin Cronk, then at the University of Cambridge. At a later date, Benjamin obtained cuttings of the ebony by lowering his brother Charlie down the cliff on a rope; all the plants in cultivation today are believed to be descended from this daring collection. The cuttings were successfully rooted at Cambridge Botanic Garden, and from there distributed to the Royal Botanic Gardens, Kew, and some 25 sites worldwide.

George Benjamin rediscovered not only the St Helena ebony but also the St Helena olive (*Nesiota elliptica*), the last remaining wild tree of which died in 1994, and the last cultivated tree in 2003. One of 11 children, he worked first in one of the island's flax mills and later as a forest guard and conservation officer, protecting St Helena's flora until his retirement in 1995. He was awarded the British Empire Medal in 1989.

Specimen notes | Received from Ness Botanic Garden, Liverpool, in 1986. The current plants are seven-year-old cuttings from the original.

Location | Edinburgh (Glasshouses).

Conservation status | CR

Trochetiopsis ebenus is not related to the true ebonies (*Diospyros*), but the hard, black wood from which it gets its name was used to make household furniture, utensils and ornaments; in the nineteenth century it was used as fuel in lime kilns to make mortar wood. It is so dense that it is said to sink in water.

St Helena's national flower, this is the only Trochetiopsis to have survived extinction in the wild.

The almost total annihilation of the St Helena ebony occurred before 1800, predating most of the island's botanical records and leaving little direct evidence of its cause. Goats – introduced by Portuguese sailors in the early sixteenth century – are very likely to have been a major factor. They thrived in large numbers until their virtual eradication in the second half of the twentieth century.

The St Helena ebony grows well from both seed and cuttings, and a propagation and reintroduction programme has generated a population of a few thousand plants on the island, at sites including Ebony Plain, High Peak and Millennium Forest. The only other two species of *Trochetiopsis*, also unique to St Helena, have not fared so well: *T. erythroxylon*, the St Helena redwood, is now extinct in the wild, and *T. melanoxylon* is lost forever.

Paulownia kawakamii

In Japanese tradition, when a girl is born a *Paulownia* (foxglove tree) is planted near the house for good luck; when the girl marries the tree is felled and used to make her wedding chest. Even if she marries young, a sizeable chest can be made, because paulownias are some of the fastest-growing trees in the world, reaching maturity in as little as 10 years.

Native to eastern China (including Taiwan) and Japan, *Paulownia kawakamii*, 台湾泡桐, *tai wan pao tong* or the sapphire dragon tree (Paulowniaceae), was scientifically named by Tokutarô Itô (1868–1941) for Taiwanese plant collector Takiya Kawakami (1871–1915). The genus *Paulownia* is named for Anna Paulowna, queen consort of the Netherlands (1795–1865), daughter of Tsar Paul I of Russia. Its flower is now the symbol of the office of the Prime Minister of Japan.

Paulownia kawakamii has very large, softly downy, heart-shaped leaves, and large, showy pink-purple flowers in spring. In the wild the species is threatened by the clearing of its mixed evergreen forest habitat for the planting of apple and peach orchards, and by past overexploitation for its valuable timber. Strong and lightweight, it was used for musical instruments, skis and surfboards, as well as those wedding chests. At last count,

The rarest species of Paulownia, the foxglove trees.

in 1998, only 13 mature trees remained in the wild.

However, *Paulownia kawakamii* and its close relative *Paulownia tomentosa* (princess or empress tree) are widely planted outside their natural range as street trees because they are deep-rooted and, unlike many other species, do not cause damage to the surface of the road or pavement.

In the wake of the famous hurricane that hit south-east England in 1987, in the early 1990s the Royal Botanic Gardens, Kew, initiated a new wave of plant collecting to fill gaps within its collections, focused on eastern Asia. Our plant – found at Logan – is thought to result from one of those expeditions.

Specimen notes | Collected in Taiwan in 1992 and received from the Royal Botanic Gardens, Kew in 2013.

Location | Logan.

Conservation status |

14

Rhododendron adenosum

Previously considered extinct in the wild, a single individual of *Rhododendron adenosum* (枯鲁杜鹃, *ku lu du juan*), discovered in 2020 by scientists at the Yunnan Key Laboratory for Integrative Conservation of Plant Species with Extremely Small Population, keeps the species' wild hopes alive.

Rhododendron adenosum was collected in the spruce forests of the Kulu Mountains by Joseph Rock in September 1929, but not recognised as a distinct species until 1978. The plants at the Royal Botanic Garden Edinburgh – and indeed all plants in private collections and at botanic gardens around the world – are thought to be descended from Rock's collection.

Specimen notes | The plant at Edinburgh was grown from Joseph Rock's 1929 collection; others grown at Benmore and Dawyck were received from a cultivated source in 1969.

Location | Benmore; Dawyck; Edinburgh (Copse and Oak Lawn).

Conservation status |

It was not seen again in nature until its rediscovery in the Kulu Mountains of south-west Sichuan after days of concerted fieldwork. It bears the leathery leaves and clusters of pink-purple flowers typical of many of south-west China's *Rhododendrons*, and is easily overlooked.

A single shrub of this thought-to-be-extinct species was discovered in 2020.

The limited genetic base in cultivation may cause problems for the species' long-term cultivation. Efforts are underway in China to conserve the one remaining individual, target fieldwork to locate others, and to create a 'near-*situ*' collection of seed-raised plants.

Echinocactus grusonii

Echinocactus grusonii (Cactaceae) is also known as the golden barrel cactus or, tongue-in-cheek, as 'mother-in-law's cushion'. It is found in the Mexican states of Querétaro and Hidalgo, to the north of Mexico City, and was recently also identified in Zacatecas.

Growing in the subtropical semi-desert shrubland referred to as the *mattoral*, these roughly spherical plants can grow to over a metre tall. They are characterised by pronounced ribs bearing strong, sharp, yellow or white spines – hence the cheeky nickname.

The 'mother-in-law's cushion' cactus is no longer in danger of being sat upon.

Echinocactus grusonii is one of the most widely propagated of all cacti, with literally millions of individuals grown by commercial nurseries and hobbyists. In the wild, populations are in decline, with only 11,000 mature individuals remaining in isolated sites. Several of the species' populations have been destroyed by dam construction, most notably the Zimapán dam on the border of Querétaro and Hidalgo, built in the 1990s, which flooded an area of 23 square kilometres for the generation of hydroelectric power.

As with many cacti, the biggest threat to the golden barrel remains illegal collection for the horticultural trade. DNA barcoding – a genetic technique in which the sequences of small, highly variable pieces of DNA can be used to identify a species or perhaps even a population – may help in reducing illegal collection by tracing the origin of specimens traded around the world.

In addition, the Jardin Botanico Regional de Cadereyta in Querétaro is propagating the species extensively, including developing an *in-vitro* procedure which may produce new plants rapidly to satisfy the horticultural trade, reducing pressure on the wild populations.

Specimen notes | Received in 2009 as a small plant from a donor in Benmore, via David Mitchell, at the time curator of the Indoor Department.

Location | Edinburgh (Glasshouses).

Conservation status | EN

Betula chichibuensis

The Chichibu birch, *Betula chichibuensis* (Betulaceae – birch family), is one of the world's rarest birches. In the wild it is found only on the limestone mountains of central and north-east Honshu Island, Japan. Not closely related to any other birches, the species is considered an ancient, relict lineage.

In 1993, only 21 mature trees of the Chichibu birch were thought to survive, in the Chichibu Tama Kai National Park. Since 2017, additional small stands have been identified in the Kitakami Mountains of north-east Honshu.

With such small numbers of trees remaining, the Chichibu birch is susceptible not only to habitat degradation through deforestation – which is actively taking place in the Chichibu district – but also to disease and natural disasters.

The Chichibu birch bears separate male and female flowers on the same plant, but is self-incompatible, so two genetically distinct individuals are needed for cross-pollination and successful reproduction. This becomes trickier the smaller the population becomes. However, when multiple genetically distinct individuals are grown in close proximity and allowed to pollinate one another, large amounts of viable seed can be obtained.

A concerted conservation effort for the Chichibu birch has been led jointly by Oxford University Botanic Garden and Arboretum, Bedgebury Pinetum, and the University of Tokyo Forests, and included seed banking along with *ex-situ* and *in-situ* measures. A germination protocol developed at Bedgebury produced over 100 seedlings, which were widely shared amongst botanic gardens and arboreta and are now cultivated at around 40 sites worldwide.

One of the world's rarest birches.

Specimen notes | Our tree was obtained via Ness Botanic Garden, Liverpool, in 2005, and may be one of the Bedgebury seedlings.

Location | Edinburgh (Upper Birch Lawn).

Conservation status |

Rhododendron macabeanum

Rhododendron macabeanum is known as *yomutapun* ('*Rhododendron* of the cold place') to the Yimkhiung Naga who live around Mount Saramati in the Naga Hills on the India–Myanmar border. The species is recorded only from Mount Saramati and one other site in north-east India, Mount Japvo in Manipur.

It was at Mount Japvo where it was collected by Sir George Watt (1851–1930), a Scottish physician and economic botanist, in 1882. Watt drew up a description of this *Rhododendron* and tentatively named it – as a variety of *R. falconeri* – for Robert Blair McCabe (1854–1897), at the time Deputy Commissioner of Manipur and later Inspector-General of Assam, who organised the collecting trip on which the specimen was taken. McCabe came to an untimely end in the 1897 Shillong (or Great Assam) Earthquake.

> *This 'Rhododendron of the cold place' is right at home in Scotland.*

The species was formally described, based on Watt's account and collections, by Sir Isaac Bayley Balfour (1853–1922) in 1920, at which time he was Regius Keeper of the Royal Botanic Garden Edinburgh.

Rhododendron macabeanum is a large evergreen shrub or small tree, which can form dense, dwarf forests. It bears large leaves, shiny above and woolly beneath, and huge clusters of eye-catching yellow flowers with a bright red stigma at their centre. Although it can be common at its two sites, it is at risk from habitat loss due to logging of the surrounding forests.

Conservation of this species is led by the Botanical Survey of India. Successful tissue-culture protocols have been developed to generate large numbers of plants from seed, and these plants are now being reintroduced to bolster wild populations.

At the Royal Botanic Garden Edinburgh, this *Rhododendron* grows well at both the Edinburgh and Benmore gardens, and one Edinburgh specimen is considered a British Champion Tree.

Specimen notes | Multiple plants, most of unknown provenance, received from 1953 onwards.

Location | Benmore; Edinburgh (Woodland Garden).

Conservation status | EN

Xanthocyparis vietnamensis

Xanthocyparis vietnamensis (Cupressaceae), the Vietnamese golden cypress, is restricted in the wild to the rugged limestone karst mountains of northern Vietnam and neighbouring China.

It was formally described in 2002, following its discovery in the Bat Dai Son Nature Reserve of Hagiang province, northern Vietnam, in 1999. Since then, it has been discovered in other provinces of the karst limestone areas of northern Vietnam and in Guangxi, China.

This slow-growing, small conifer has very distinctive prickly juvenile foliage, which often occurs in combination with the markedly different adult foliage. Initially assessed as critically endangered, it has been downgraded (or should that be promoted?) to endangered, as additional stands were found in Vietnam and China.

Specimen notes | Multiple trees obtained from the wild by the International Conifer Conservation Programme between 2002 and 2012 via cuttings. Most are now growing at International Conifer Conservation Programme safe sites around the British Isles, but a few remain at Benmore, Edinburgh and Logan.

Location | Benmore; Edinburgh (Chinese Border); Logan.

Conservation status | EN

The Vietnamese golden cypress is highly prized for its fine, yellow-brown, very hard and fragrant timber, which puts it increasingly at risk. Although forest clearance for agriculture is unlikely to reach the steep ridges where the species grows, clearance of the forests below increases the risk of fires spreading to the upper slopes of the mountains. Acid rain from nearby industrialised parts of China may also be having an impact, particularly in winter when the dominant winds tend to come from the north-east.

The golden cypress remained hidden in the craggy mountains of Southeast Asia until 1999.

The Royal Botanic Garden Edinburgh's International Conifer Conservation Programme is engaged in an intensive programme of *ex-situ* conservation for the Vietnamese golden cypress, introduced the species to cultivation in the UK in 2002, and is growing the tree at safe sites around the British Isles. In Vietnam, the species is protected, and restoration work has been undertaken in the Bat Dai Son area.

Salix lanata

Salix lanata (Salicaceae – willow family), the woolly willow, is one of Scotland's most iconic mountain plants. A widespread subarctic species, in the UK it is restricted to a few small, vulnerable populations in the Scottish Highlands where the land is north-facing and the snow lies late – conditions which are becoming rarer by the year as the effects of climate change intensify.

In addition to climate change, the woolly willow is vulnerable to grazing, particularly as snow cover is needed to protect the plants from nibbling animals in the early spring. With separate male and female plants, successful reproduction of the species requires the two to be within around 50 metres of each other. Some unfortunate populations such as that on Ben Lawers contain only one sex, and are therefore functionally extinct.

Threatened by climate change, protected by knitwear.

Pioneering work to restore Scotland's montane willows, including *S. lanata*, has been carried out by the National Trust for Scotland since 1987. Exclosures were put in place to prevent grazing and monitor regeneration, and rooted cuttings grown on their Meall na Samhna estate were replanted.

In the early 2000s, the Scottish Government/NatureScot Species Action Framework provided additional funding to protect selected species, including woolly willow. A dedicated shade tunnel was installed at the Royal Botanic Garden Edinburgh for *ex-situ* propagation of this and other rare Scottish species.

Subsequently, Edinburgh-grown plants were planted out at Corrie Garbhlach – where climbers had to use ropes to access the steep planting areas – and Corrie Sharroch, off Corrie Fee, which the Royal Botanic Garden Edinburgh continues to monitor. More than 1,000 willow plants have been translocated over the years, with care being taken to maximise genetic diversity by taking cuttings from many parent plants, and to minimise biosecurity risks by maintaining strict plant health and quarantine measures.

The young leaves of *S. lanata* are covered with a delightfully soft, white 'wool' – the source of both common and scientific names (*lanata* being from the Latin for woolly). This has made for an interesting link with the knitwear designer Sarah Clarkson of Edinburgh-based Woolly Originals. Sarah's 'Save the willow' range, developed in collaboration with the Royal Botanic Garden Edinburgh, helps raise funds for our work to protect the woolly willow.

Specimen notes | Multiple examples grown from wild-collected seed can be viewed at Benmore, Dawyck and Edinburgh – although thousands more can now be seen in the Highlands.

Location | Benmore; Dawyck; Edinburgh (Demonstration and Rock Gardens).

Conservation status | VU (UK)

Brahea edulis

Brahea edulis (Arecaceae) – the *palma de Guadalupe* – is found in the wild only on Guadalupe Island off Baja California, Mexico, where it grows on steep, rocky slopes and survives on the little moisture provided by the frequent fogs coming in from the Pacific Ocean.

The *palma de Guadalupe* is a fan palm with – unsurprisingly – distinctive fan-shaped leaves, about 20 of which are borne on a rather stocky trunk. The epithet *edulis* derives from the Latin for 'edible' and generally denotes a plant at least part of which, is good to eat. In the case of the *palma de Guadalupe,* the sweet fruits are delicious fresh or made into jam – or eaten, seeds and all, by goats.

Guadalupe Island boasts fewer than 150 human residents – mostly scientists, military weather station personnel, and a small group of seasonal fishers – and, at one time, 100,000 feral goats, introduced during the nineteenth century by whalers as a stopover food. Having decimated the flora of the island, the goat population crashed and finally settled at between 10 and 20,000.

Specimen notes | Received as a seed from Valencia Botanic Garden in 2008.

Location | Edinburgh (Glasshouses).

Conservation status | EN

By 2000, regeneration of the *palma de Guadalupe* had essentially stalled for more than a century due to the goats, leaving an entire wild population of little more than 1,000 old trees, described by the IUCN as "moribund".

Had a narrow escape from goat-induced annihilation.

Between 2000 and 2007 the Mexican government installed a series of goat-proof fences and carried out a comprehensive goat-eradication programme. In 2005 Guadalupe Island and its surrounding waters and islets were declared a Special Biosphere Reserve with the aim of restoring the lost vegetation.

Unlike many species which had already been driven into extinction (at low altitudes, the *palma de Guadalupe* is essentially the only remaining tree to be seen on the island), it is thought that the *palma de Guadalupe* will eventually recover, although there is a risk that introduced weeds may compete with the palm seedlings, and soil erosion initiated by the goats remains a potential threat.

Juniperus bermudiana

Bermuda's national tree, and endemic to the island, *Juniperus bermudiana* (Bermuda juniper or Bermuda red cedar) has been overexploited since the island was first colonised in 1609, for firewood and to construct anything from houses and churches to ships and coffins.

The juniper's berry-like cones were historically eaten and used to make a medicinal syrup. To this day they are used in wardrobes to repel mildew, moths and other insects.

Bermuda red cedar wood is remarkably lightweight, yet highly resistant to decay and insects. This makes it exceptionally good for building boats. The 'Bermuda sloops' once used by the British Royal Navy were speedy, agile, and would last for 20 years or more at sea. HMS *Pickle*, the first ship to bring the news of Admiral Lord Nelson's victory and death at the Battle of Trafalgar to the British at Falmouth, was a red cedar Bermuda sloop.

Legislation was put in place as early as 1622 to control the export of Bermuda red cedar wood, but shipbuilding continued until the 1830s. After 1900, the shipbuilding industry declined, construction began to use cheaper imported timber from the USA, and rural electrification limited the wood's use as a cooking fuel. By the early 1940s *J. bermudiana* had made an almost full recovery.

A further blow was dealt to the species over a single decade from 1946–1956 when almost 95 per cent of the wild population was lost due to the introduction of a double-whammy of pests, juniper scale insect (*Carulaspis minima*) and oyster-shell scale (*Lepidosaphes ulmi*), via ornamental *Juniper* species from California. As the Bermuda red cedar population crashed again, its place in the landscape was rapidly filled by introduced species like Asia's *Casuarina equisitifolia* (whistling pine tree).

Since 1980, a combination of residual resistance (some five per cent of Bermuda red cedars seem largely immune to the scale insects), intensive reafforestation and natural regeneration has begun to restore the species' numbers once again. The current population is estimated to be over 10,000 adult trees, possibly as many as 25,000, which would equate to roughly 10 per cent of its former population density. The Bermuda red cedar is slowly but surely coming back from the brink.

> *Bermuda's national tree has bounced back from not one, but two, brushes with extinction.*

Specimen notes | Our first plants were received 1991 and distributed to International Conifer Conservation Programme safe sites at the Sir Harold Hillier Gardens and Arboretum and Logan Estate, Dumfries and Galloway; in 1994 further seed from Bermuda was planted in Edinburgh.

Location | Edinburgh (not on public display).

Conservation status |

Liquidambar orientalis

Liquidambar orientalis (Altingiaceae) – *günlük ağacı*, Oriental sweetgum, or Turkish sweetgum – is the lesser-known cousin of the popular and widespread ornamental American sweetgum, *Liquidambar styraciflua*, and displays equally lovely autumn foliage.

The Oriental sweetgum, now found only on the Greek island of Rhodes and in south-west Turkey, is the traditional source of antiseptic balsam, tapped from the bark, as well as sweetgum oil which is used for stabilising perfumes. Now largely made synthetically, both products are still economically important locally, where the species is also used for firewood. In Turkey, the trees have additional spiritual significance, with the bark being burned as incense at funerals and celebrations. *Liquidambar orientalis* groves are held as sacred sites in the spring festival of Nevruz.

Specimen notes | Edinburgh's oldest plant, on the *Pyrus* Lawn, was grown from seed collected in Turkey in 1986; another was supplied by the Sir Harold Hillier Gardens and Arboretum in 2004. In 2016 a cutting was grown from the 1986 specimen and is now planted at Dawyck.

Location | Dawyck; Edinburgh (*Pyrus* Lawn, Woodland Garden, *Rhododendron* Walk).

Conservation status |

In both Greece and Turkey, the sweetgum is threatened by land clearance for agriculture, particularly citrus production. Droughts and water-table disruption caused by climate change and dam construction, grazing by goats which prevents natural regeneration, and – on Rhodes – trampling by tourists, have all also led to declines in the species' numbers.

A source of incense, balsam and sweetgum.

The Oriental sweetgum is protected in some areas – in Rhodes as an incidental by-product of protection put in place for *Euplagia quadripunctaria* (Jersey tiger moth) – and tourism on Rhodes is now well-managed to prevent trampling. The Turkish Forestry Service runs an active conservation programme to prevent overexploitation, and maintains gene conservation forests and a seed orchard to support *ex-situ* conservation efforts. The IUCN now records this endangered species as 'stable'.

Woodsia ilvensis

The oblong woodsia (Woodsiaceae – cliff fern family), *Woodsia ilvensis*, is Britain's rarest fern.

The species was devastated through over-collecting in the nineteenth century during the Victorian fern craze dubbed by writer Charles Kingsley (1819–1875) as 'pteridomania' (fern-fever) in his 1855 work *Glaucus, or the Wonders of the Shore.*

The UK's rarest fern, all-but wiped out by Victorian fern fever.

Very small populations – often comprising only four or fewer plants – of the oblong woodsia still exist in Scotland and Wales, with one larger population of 60–100 plants surviving at a single location in England. Largely confined to steep cliffs, such tiny populations could easily be wiped out by a rock fall.

Using plants from Canada, Iceland, Norway and Russia, as well as the UK, research is underway at the Royal Botanic Garden Edinburgh to help prevent the oblong woodsia from disappearing from Scotland altogether. Collecting the species is now generally illegal, but spores have been collected from all British populations under licence by conservation agencies, to investigate how natural regeneration might be enhanced, and a huge *ex-situ* collection of plants is now in cultivation.

Reintroductions have been made to sites where oblong woodsia was recorded in the past in both Teesdale, England, and Scotland's Southern Uplands, and these continue to be monitored regularly.

Specimen notes | A large *ex-situ* population grown from spores collected under licence from all UK sites, with a few from further afield.

Location | Edinburgh.

Conservation status | EN (UK)

Abies nebrodensis

Also known as the Sicilian fir or Nebrodi fir, *Abies nebrodensis* (Pinaceae) is a broad, conical conifer with spreading horizontal branches, seen only in north-central Sicily.

Previously distributed right across the island's Madonie Mountains, confusingly once called the 'Nebrodes' which gave rise to the species' scientific name (the Nebrodi mountains are actually further east), by 1900 the Sicilian fir was thought to be extinct in the wild following extensive logging for construction, and erosion of its mountain habitat.

Specimen notes | Grown from wild collections made in Sicily in 1993 and 2003.

Location | Benmore; Dawyck.

Conservation status |

It was rediscovered in 1957, and today ranks as one of the most threatened conifers in the world, with just 32 adult trees (only 25 of them fertile) scattered and clinging to the denuded, steep north-west-facing limestone slope of Monte Scalone in the Madonie Regional Park.

Once believed to be extinct, we now have hope for this species' future.

There are, however, around 155 young plants which will, with care, continue to thrive.

An extensive *ex-situ* conservation programme for the Sicilian fir has been in place for a number of years, with trees planted in the Orto Botanico di Palermo, in the gardens of villas in the Madonie Mountains, and distributed to other botanic gardens and arboreta in Europe, including the Royal Botanic Garden Edinburgh. Our Dawyck site held 12 trees, although a pathogen attack in 2021 meant that four of these, sadly, had to be removed.

In 2005, *A. nebrodensis* was featured in the IUCN's '*Top 50 Mediterranean Island Plants: wild plants at the brink of extinction and what is needed to save them*'. A reassessment of these 50 species a decade on found that the survival prospects had improved for 21 species, and worsened for only one. Although the Sicilian fir has not been moved from critically endangered to endangered yet, as the population continues to regenerate this is looking a good bet for the future.

Cicerbita alpina

The striking blue flowers of *Cicerbita alpina* (Asteraceae – daisy family), the alpine-blue sowthistle, are held on 1.5-metre-tall stems. Yet this conspicuous plant is hard to spot unless you know where to look.

One of the UK's largest and rarest arctic-montane species, *C. alpina* is found wild in only four very small populations, hidden away on steep cliff ledges in the Cairngorms National Park, out of reach of sheep and deer. At least eight populations have been lost over the past two centuries, the most recent extinction being at Canness Glen in the Grampian Mountains in 1978.

Cerulean-blue flowers hide their beauty in the most inaccessible places.

The alpine-blue sowthistle is rather more widespread in Europe, particularly in Scandinavia. Related to lettuce and chicory, this species is very palatable to a range of animals – from slugs to sheep to even bears – and is also consumed by humans in central Europe. The edible shoots are rich in caffeic acid derivatives, similar to those found in coffee.

In Scotland, the species is threatened not by coffee-drinkers but by deforestation, habitat loss, climate change and overgrazing. It is also at risk from catastrophic events such as landslides, and suffers from low levels of natural regeneration.

A long-term project at the Royal Botanic Garden Edinburgh has uncovered low levels of genetic variation within each of the Scottish populations, which may be hampering natural regeneration. Our scientists and horticulturists are working to build a comprehensive picture of this charismatic species' biology, ecological requirements, germination and cultivation, which is informing practical conservation efforts.

Several new populations have been planted, in collaboration with local landowners and conservation partners, using our *ex-situ* collections, to prevent the species from becoming extinct in the wild – and the sowthistle is no longer so difficult to find: just stand on the bridge at Braemar and look down!

Specimen notes | Large numbers of plants grown as part of our conservation breeding programme, from collections made and cultivated since 1999, including representatives of all four Scottish populations as well as plants from Norway.

Location | Dawyck; Edinburgh (Rain Garden and elsewhere).

Conservation status | VU (UK)

Ginkgo biloba

Ginkgo biloba (Ginkgoaceae), in China known as 银杏, *yin xing*, and elsewhere as the maidenhair tree, is the sole survivor of an ancient lineage dating back more than two million years. As Peter Crane, once Director of the Royal Botanic Gardens, Kew, and author of *Ginkgo: The Tree That Time Forgot* puts it, "there are only five living groups of seed plants, and *Ginkgo* is one of them". The others are the flowering plants, conifers, cycads and the wonderfully bizarre Gnetales.

That puts *Ginkgo* squarely in 'living fossil' territory. The genus was once widespread throughout the northern hemisphere, with fossil *Ginkgo* species (*G. gardneri*) even having been discovered in Scotland, on the Isle of Mull. In fact, the maidenhair tree was itself once thought to be extinct in the wild until a natural population was rediscovered on Xitianmu in Zhejing, China.

Ginkgo biloba is widely planted and easy to spot: no other tree has those fan-shaped leaves with open, forked veins. It is also in widespread use as a food supplement and herbal medicine, in energy drinks and to combat conditions from altitude sickness to dementia.

The trees are dioecious – existing in male and female forms. The females are less frequently planted because their fruit produces a rancid smell when fallen – not a desirable characteristic in a street tree. Nonetheless, the seeds from *Ginkgo* fruits are often eaten in Asia, although they can be toxic if ingested in large quantities.

The living fossil that survived a nuclear blast.

Unlike most of the species in this book, the reasons for the maidenhair tree's rarity in the wild are not fully understood and are not necessarily due to human activity. It is possible that this ancient lineage was simply outcompeted by flowering plants. Its conservation has been almost equally inadvertent, through human cultivation on a small scale at first around temples and for the seeds in China, then across the world as an ornamental after its introduction to Europe in the late seventeenth century. One of the few living things to survive the atomic bomb dropped on Hiroshima in 1945, *Ginkgo biloba* is certainly a survivor.

Specimen notes | Several trees, of garden and possible wild origin. Our oldest dates from 1892 and can be seen at Edinburgh.

Location | Benmore; Edinburgh (Fossil Lawn).

Conservation status | EN

Wollemia nobilis

Wollemia nobilis (Araucariaceae), the Wollemi pine, was until 1994 known only from fossils and was believed to be extinct. This exceptional conifer was discovered by a group of canyoners led by David Noble – now immortalised in the plant's name – in a remote gorge in the Blue Mountains of New South Wales, Australia, less than 200 kilometres from Sydney.

Reaching heights of nearly 40 metres, the Wollemi pine is an impressive tree with a distinct, four-ranked leaf arrangement that marks it out from all other conifers. The natural range of the species is kept secret, but covers fewer than 100 square kilometres of deep, narrow sandstone gorges in warm temperate rainforest surrounded by *Eucalyptus* woodland. There are currently estimated to be 80 mature individuals and around 300 seedlings and juveniles in the wild. In 2000 the pre-existing Wollemi National Park was inscribed as one of eight protected areas forming the UNESCO World Heritage-listed Greater Blue Mountains Area.

Wollemia, from an Aboriginal term meaning 'watch out, look around you', is a true conservation success story.

The greatest threats to the Wollemi pine at present are in fact two species of the highly infectious pathogen *Phytophthora* – *P. cinnamomi* and *P. multivora* – probably introduced by unauthorised visitors to the site. In addition, the entire population of *W. nobilis* came close to destruction in Australia's catastrophic 2019–2020 wildfire season. Only a desperate effort by specialist firefighters saved the species, leaving its grove the only green area in an otherwise devastated landscape.

Soon after its discovery, the Australian government, realising the Wollemi pine was likely at great risk from unauthorised collection, instituted a programme to establish an ample stock of nursery plants to meet the demands of collectors and botanic gardens throughout the world. The species has been exported from Australia since 2006, and has fully entered the international horticultural trade, preventing pressure on the wild population. This pre-emptive international sharing of material, which has helped maintain the wild population at a stable level despite the many threats to its existence, makes this probably one of the most successful examples of *ex-situ* conservation the world has ever seen.

Specimen notes | Plants were received in 2004, ahead of the general rollout by the Australian government. Logan's Wollemi pines were the first to be planted outdoors in Scotland, in 2006, and are now some of the largest, despite sustaining considerable damage during 2018's Storm Ali.

Location | Benmore; Edinburgh; Logan.

Conservation status | CR

Index to scientific names